PRENTICE
LITERATURE

PENGUIN EDITION

Teaching Resources

Unit 6
Themes in American Stories

Grade Eight

PEARSON

Prentice
Hall

Upper Saddle River, New Jersey
Boston, Massachusetts

PEARSON

Prentice
Hall

ISBN 0-13-190789-1

1 2 3 4 5 6 7 8 9 10   09 08 07 06 05

Contents

Part 1 Summarize

"Water Names" by Lan Samantha Chang

"Why the Waves Have Whitecaps" by Zora Neale Hurston

"Coyote Steals the Sun and Moon" retold by Richard Erdoes and Alfonso Ortiz

Part 2 Purpose for Reading

"An Episode of War" by Stephen Crane

from **My Own True Name** by Pat Mora

"Words to Sit In, Like Chairs" by Naomi Shihab Nye

Vocabulary Warm-up Word Lists

Study these words from "Water Names." Then, complete the activities.

Word List A

abruptness [uh BRUPT nuhs] *n.* a way of ending things suddenly
   When Dad shouted, I ended my telephone call with <u>abruptness</u>.

bulk [BUHLK] *n.* the large size of something
   The <u>bulk</u> of a ship that carries people across the ocean is amazing.

forbidden [fuhr BID in] *adj.* not allowed
   <u>Forbidden</u> to drive the car, I took the train into the city.

glittered [GLIT uhrd] *v.* shone with a sparkling light
   Her eyes <u>glittered</u> from the tears she held back.

gorges [GAWRJ ez] *n.* deep, narrow valleys cut through rock
   <u>Gorges</u> are cut through rocks by water moving through them over thousands of years.

reflection [ri FLEK shuhn] *n.* image you see when you look in a mirror or shiny surface
   The small boy was surprised to see his <u>reflection</u> in the shiny bumper of the new car.

remote [ri MOHT] *adj.* far away
   The wealthy, unhappy man chose to live alone on a <u>remote</u> island.

rippling [RIP uh ling] *adj.* having small waves on the surface
   The <u>rippling</u> water relaxed me as I sat by the stream.

Word List B

blackening [BLAK uhn ing] *adj.* becoming darker or more black
   Watching the <u>blackening</u> sky with worry, Meg hurried to get home.

countless [KOWNT luhs] *adj.* very many; too many to count
   If there are <u>countless</u> stars in the sky, why do people search for new ones?

delta [DEL tuh] *n.* low, triangular piece of land where a river meets the sea
   A <u>delta</u>, with its rich soil, is a good place to grow crops such as rice.

flecked [FLEKT] *adj.* having small marks or spots
   Since the puppy was <u>flecked</u> with black, we named her Dot.

fulfilled [fool FILD] *v.* gotten or done something that you hoped for
   My desire for a new friend was <u>fulfilled</u> when Jeff arrived.

gutted [GUHT id] *v.* removed the organs of a fish to cook it.
   I liked catching fish, but I never watched them <u>gutted</u>.

sleek [SLEEK] *adj.* having a smooth, attractive and graceful shape
   The completely black horse was <u>sleek</u> and loved to run.

wavy [WAY vee] *adj.* having a little bit of curl
   Why do people with straight hair often work hard to make it <u>wavy</u>?

"Water Names" by Lan Samantha Chang
Vocabulary Warm-up Exercises

Exercise A *Fill in each blank in the paragraph below with an appropriate word from Word List A. Use each word only once.*

As we turned the corner, the [1] _____ of the mountain rose up

suddenly before us. Below it, a lake [2] _____ brightly in the sunlight.

The water was as smooth as a mirror. As I looked, I could see the mountain's

[3] _____ in it. I had heard that small fingers of the lake pushed into

deep [4] _____ along the sides of the mountain. Because many of these

areas were private, visitors were [5] _____ there. We rolled down the car

windows to feel the fresh breeze and listen to the [6] _____ water. Since

we were miles from any town, we noticed the quiet of this [7] _____ area

right away. With [8] _____, we forgot the stress of our busy city life and

relaxed at last.

Exercise B *Revise the sentences so that each underlined word is used in a logical way. Be sure to keep the vocabulary words in your revisions.*

1. Lil wanted a <u>sleek</u> car so she bought one that had a square, clunky look.

   _____

2. Each morning when my alarm goes off, I look out my window at the <u>blackening</u> sky.

   _____

3. Having <u>fulfilled</u> her wish to win an award, the actress cried tears of sadness.

   _____

4. Since we did not plan to eat the fish, we <u>gutted</u> it and set it free in the sea.

   _____

5. About halfway along the river's path, you can see a huge <u>delta</u>.

   _____

6. Mom wanted a solid black sweater, so I bought one <u>flecked</u> with blue and red.

   _____

7. Because I had <u>countless</u> good reasons to go to the party, I chose to stay home.

   _____

8. Anna liked her <u>wavy</u> hair, so she always tried to straighten it.

   _____

2

Name _____ Date _____

"Water Names" by Lan Samantha Chang
Reading Warm-up A

Read the following passage. Pay special attention to the underlined words. Then, read it again, and complete the activities. Use a separate sheet of paper for your written answers.

The Yangtze River in China is the third longest river in the world. It flows more than 3,700 miles, through cities, towns, and <u>remote</u> areas that few people ever see. The scenery along the river is some of the most beautiful on Earth. The river has <u>glittered</u> like a jewel in the hearts and minds of Chinese people for centuries. Today, more than 350 million people live along its shores.

Although the Yangtze gives people important gifts, it also can kill them. With the <u>abruptness</u> that comes from sudden flooding, whole villages can be wiped out. At these times, the <u>rippling</u> waters become a raging enemy. Animals, people, and all other living things are at risk. As waters rise, the high walls of deep <u>gorges</u> can suddenly seem low. Terror strikes all along the banks of the swollen river.

To control the floods, the Chinese government has built dams along the Yangtze. The biggest of these projects is the Three Gorges Dam. Begun in 1994, the dam should be finished in 2009. The planned <u>bulk</u> of it is amazing. It will be one and a half miles wide and 610 feet tall. The lake it creates will hold five trillion gallons of water. Electricity produced by the dam will meet one-ninth of China's needs.

Not everyone is happy about the project. However, Chinese people, <u>forbidden</u> to speak out against the government, keep their opinions to themselves. Nearly two million people, however, will have to find new homes as the dam waters rise. Some types of wildlife could be wiped out forever.

Most agree that the Three Gorges Dam will have both advantages and disadvantages. No matter what happens, the mighty Yangtze will continue to be important to China. Whether looking at a <u>reflection</u> in a peaceful spot, fishing, or taking water from the river for farming, Chinese people will continue to be thankful for this grand gift of nature.

1. Underline the words that give a clue about the meaning of <u>remote</u>. Then, write your own definition of *remote*.

2. Circle the words describing how the river has <u>glittered</u>. Then, explain what *glittered* means.

3. Underline the words naming the source of the <u>abruptness</u> that is described. Then, tell about another natural disaster that comes with *abruptness*.

4. Circle two words naming one feature of <u>gorges</u>. Then, explain what *gorges* are.

5. Underline all the words in the paragraph describing the <u>bulk</u> of the Three Gorges Dam. Then, describe the *bulk* of something huge you have seen.

6. Circle the words naming what the Chinese people are <u>forbidden</u> to do. Then, explain what *forbidden* means.

7. Circle the word that gives a clue to the meaning of <u>reflection</u>. Describe two different types of *reflections* that you might see in the Yangtze River.

"Water Names" by Lan Samantha Chang
Reading Warm-up B

Read the following passage. Pay special attention to the underlined words. Then, read it again, and complete the activities. Use a separate sheet of paper for your written answers.

Grandfather Pin tells us <u>countless</u> stories of his childhood in China. My favorites always seem to feature the mighty Yangtze River.

Grandfather grew up near Shanghai, the huge city at the mouth of the river, where the Yangtze empties into the Yellow Sea. His relatives were not city people, though. They worked as rice farmers. The huge, rich <u>delta</u> of the Yangtze made rice farming possible. Grandfather says the river gave his family life.

Grandfather's river stories describe the water in different ways. Sometimes, the river has graceful curves and bends that give it a <u>sleek</u> appearance. The water moves silently and swiftly below the surface. Sometimes, the river is <u>wavy</u>, not like an ocean, but like my friend Kelsey's hair. The water is bumpy and seems to be grumbling in these stories.

The color of the water changes in Grandfather's stories, too. In tales set high in the mountains, the river is <u>flecked</u> with gold that shimmers in the sunlight. For stories set in the lowlands, the river is darker in color. Strange dramas often happen in these stories. Huge fish are caught and strange characters have <u>gutted</u> them. Other people drown as the waters lure them into the deeps. In one of these stories, the river might be changing from the dark green of an emerald to the velvet blue of a sapphire. The color might even be <u>blackening</u> to resemble the dark, sparkling beads of Grandma's favorite necklace. Always beautiful, the river is like a gem, the true hero of the stories.

When I have dreams to be <u>fulfilled</u>, I often close my eyes and try to see the river that gave my family life. Others might wish on a faraway star, but I wish on the distant Yangtze River of my grandfather's stories.

1. Underline the words naming the <u>countless</u> things mentioned in this sentence. Then, explain what *countless* means.

2. Circle the words naming what the Yangtze <u>delta</u> made possible. Then, describe a *delta*.

3. Underline the words that hint at the meaning of <u>sleek</u>. Then, describe something *sleek* you have seen.

4. Explain the difference between <u>wavy</u> water and *wavy* hair.

5. Circle the word naming what the river is <u>flecked</u> with. Then, write a sentence using *flecked*.

6. Circle the word that tells what was <u>gutted</u>. Then, describe what you've done if you have *gutted* something.

7. If water is <u>blackening</u> to resemble dark beads, what do you think these beads might look like?

8. Underline the word naming what is to be <u>fulfilled</u>. Then, tell about something you want *fulfilled* or that has been *fulfilled*.

Name _____ Date _____

Lan Samantha Chang
Listening and Viewing

Segment 1: Meet Lan Samantha Chang
• How has Lan Samantha Chang's experiences with music affected her writing? Why do you think it is important to practice writing every day?

_____

_____

_____

_____

Segment 2: Themes in Literature
• According to Lan Samantha Chang, why was storytelling important to the Chinese culture? Why do you think folk tales and fairy tales are important to society?

_____

_____

_____

_____

Segment 3: The Writing Process
• Through writing, how does Lan Samantha Chang "make a riddle out of an answer"? How do you think writing can help you learn more about something that you do not understand?

_____

_____

_____

_____

Segment 4: The Rewards of Writing
• How has writing stories based on her own family experiences been rewarding to Lan Samantha Chang? How do you think writing stories could be rewarding for you?

_____

_____

_____

_____

Learning About American Stories

Folk tradition includes the manners, customs, sayings, and stories of a culture. The American folk tradition grew out of **oral tradition**—stories and histories that were originally shared by word of mouth rather than in print. Here are some characteristics of oral tradition:

- A **theme** is an idea revealed in a tale. A **universal theme**—for example, the power of love—shows up in stories of different cultures and periods.
- **Heroes** and **heroines** are larger-than-life figures whose virtues and achievements are celebrated in the oral tradition.
- **Storytelling techniques** maintain the interest of live audiences. Techniques include

  - **Hyperbole:** exaggeration or overstatement, either to create humor or to express heightened emotion
  - **Personification:** figurative language that gives a personality and human characteristics to nonhuman subjects, such as animals or natural elements
  - **Idioms:** in a language, region, community, or class, the expressions that cannot be understood literally—for example, "cut the mustard"

Here are types of literature that began in the oral tradition:

- **Myths:** tales that use gods, goddesses, and heroes to explain the causes of natural phenomena. Every culture has its own collection of myths, or **mythology.**
- **Epics:** long narrative poems about larger-than-life heroes who engage in dangerous journeys, or **quests,** that are important to the history of a nation or culture
- **Fables:** brief stories with animals that speak and act like humans. Fables often end with a directly stated **moral,** or message.
- **Tall tales:** folk tales that use **hyperbole.** Featuring a hero who performs impossible feats, tall tales are forms of **legends,** which are based on facts but that become more fictionalized with each telling.

DIRECTIONS: *Circle the letter of the answer choice that best matches each numbered item.*

1. a story about a the Greek goddess Athena
   A. myth   B. tall tale   C. fable
2. a long narrative poem about a hero's journey home from a war
   A. fable   B. epic   C. idiom
3. the description of nonhuman subjects as if they were human
   A. personification   B. hyperbole   C. symbolism
4. story about a sly fox who outwits a crow
   A. epic   B. tall tale   C. fable
5. fictionalized, exaggerated story with a factual or historical basis
   A. legend   B. fable   C. epic
6. collection of myths
   A. folk tradition   B. mythology   C. oral tradition

"Water Names" by Lan Samantha Chang
Model Selection: American Stories

By its very nature, **folk tradition** is a living body of customs, manners, stories, and sayings that constantly changes. For example, as a story is retold over generations—either orally or in writing—new characters may appear. In the United States, nineteenth-century folk heroes included patriots, soldiers, farmers, and cowboys. A century later, American heroes came to include sports figures, politicians, businesspeople, and astronauts.

A. DIRECTIONS: *Use the space below each question about "Water Names" to write your answer.*

1. As noted above, a folk tale was often passed along orally before it was written down. When and where did Waipuo herself first hear the tale she tells her granddaughters?

   _____

   _____

2. Waipuo and her granddaughters live on the American prairie, far from a river such as the one in the story. So of what use is the story about the river to the girls?

   _____

   _____

3. Which details in "Water Names" show Waipuo's pride in the family heritage? Which details show that the family has a special relationship with the Yangtze River?

   _____

   _____

   _____

   _____

4. Identify at least two specific times when Lily reacts to or asks a question about Waipuo's story. What do these interruptions of Lily's remind us about the folk tradition?

   _____

   _____

5. What elements of Waipuo's story might explain why it has been told and retold as part of the family's folk tradition?

   _____

   _____

   _____

   _____

"Water Names" by Lan Samantha Chang
Selection Test A

Learning About American Stories *Identify the letter of the choice that best answers the question.*

_____ 1. What is the correct term for a long narrative poem about a larger-than-life hero?
A. myth
B. epic
C. tall tale
D. fable

_____ 2. Which of the following is the definition of *idiom*?
A. a story featuring animal characters
B. a central insight or message
C. an expression that cannot be understood literally
D. an exaggeration

_____ 3. Which of the following led to the American folk tradition?
A. oral tradition
B. universal themes
C. ancient epics
D. Greek and Roman mythology

_____ 4. What term means "exaggeration or overstatement"?
A. personification
B. irony
C. symbolism
D. hyperbole

_____ 5. Which of the following terms names a kind of literature that uses *hyperbole*?
A. personification
B. fables
C. tall tales
D. quests

Critical Reading

_____ 6. In "Water Names," who make up the audience for the grandmother's tale?
A. neighbors gathering on the back porch
B. the narrator's classmates
C. the grandmother's sisters
D. the narrator and her two sisters

____ 7. In "Water Names," what is the children's attitude toward Waipuo?
  A. indifferent
  B. jealous
  C. respectful
  D. angry

____ 8. What is the setting of the tale Waipuo tells in "Water Names"?
  A. near the Yangtze River in ancient China
  B. the Himalaya mountains
  C. the prairie in summertime
  D. a cruise boat on the Yangtze River

____ 9. In "Water Names," what hint does Waipuo give about the Yangtze River when she starts to tell about Wen Zhiqing's daughter?
  A. It can be dangerous.
  B. It is muddy.
  C. It is the subject of many legends.
  D. Its fish are poisoned.

____ 10. In "Water Names," what does Wen Zhiqing's daughter think about the pearl ring?
  A. She thinks that the fish attacked a young man and stole the ring from him.
  B. She thinks that an underwater prince has sent the ring as a marriage proposal.
  C. She thinks that the cormorant found the pearl in an oyster.
  D. She believes that the pearl ring is a sign that the gods love her.

____ 11. In "Water Names," what does Wen Zhiqing's daughter do when a terrible flood occurs?
  A. She goes inside the house and shuts the doors.
  B. She escapes to the city of Nanjing.
  C. She hurries to the river to visit her beloved and then disappears.
  D. She begs her father to rescue her.

____ 12. In "Water Names," what does Waipuo suggest about Wen Zhiqing's daughter?
  A. The girl was disobedient and deserved her fate.
  B. The girl probably died in the flood.
  C. The girl was too willing to give in to her own desires.
  D. The girl's personality demonstrated the strength of the family's ancestors.

_____ 13. Which of the following statements proves that Waipuo's tale in "Water Names" is part of an oral tradition?

A. Waipuo heard the tale from her own grandmother.

B. The story takes place a long time ago.

C. The tale contains supernatural elements.

D. The story includes vivid imagery.

_____ 14. The climax of a story is the turning point or the point of greatest emotional intensity. What is the climax of the tale about Wen Zhiqing's daughter in "Water Names"?

A. the discovery of the pearl ring

B. the girl's claim that a kingdom exists under the water

C. the girl's reference to a marriage proposal

D. the girl's disappearance

_____ 15. Which of the following words best describes the author Lan Samantha Chang's tone, or attitude, in "Water Names"?

A. regretful

B. mysterious

C. mocking

D. resentful

Essay

16. Write an essay in which you describe and comment on Wen Zhiqing's daughter in "Water Names." To do so, answer the following questions: What are the daughter's most striking character traits? What motivates her to take her actions? What conflict does she experience? What finally happens to her, and why?

17. Take a stand on the tale about Wen Zhiqing's daughter in "Water Names." That is, tell whether (a) the tale is just a mysterious and entertaining story, (b) the tale contains a message that is a universal theme, or (c) the tale both entertains and offers a central message about human life. Support your opinion with details from the story.

"Water Names" by Lan Samantha Chang
Selection Test B

Learning About American Stories *Identify the choice that best answers the question.*

____ 1. Which of the following is the best term to express the passing of stories, histories, and sayings by word of mouth from one generation to the next?
A. hyperbole
B. universal theme
C. oral tradition
D. idiom

____ 2. Tales that explain the actions of gods, goddesses, and heroes are known as
A. tall tales.
B. fables.
C. quests.
D. myths.

____ 3. Which of the following is the best definition of *fable*?
A. a brief story featuring animals that speak and act like humans
B. a comic story with a surprise ending
C. a tale about a larger-than-life hero
D. a long narrative poem featuring a quest

____ 4. Which of the following is the correct term for exaggeration for comic effect or heightened emotion?
A. personification
B. idiom
C. hyperbole
D. tall tale

____ 5. You might expect to find *hyperbole* in all of the following EXCEPT
A. myths
B. tall tales
C. epics
D. realistic short stories

____ 6. Which of the following best defines *universal theme*?
A. a long narrative poem about a hero who undertakes a dangerous journey
B. a message about life that is true for different periods and cultures
C. an expression that cannot be understood literally
D. a depiction of a nonhuman subject with human characteristics

Critical Reading

____ 7. Why the narrator of "Water Names" and her sisters gathered on the porch at dusk?
A. to play video games
B. to hear their grandmother's stories
C. to study Chinese
D. to plan dinner

___ 8. Which statement is true about the settings in "Water Names"?
   A. Waipuo is living in China, and the tale she tells takes place in China.
   B. Waipuo now lives on the American prairie, but her tale's setting is China.
   C. The place Waipuo now lives and the place in her tale create threatening moods.
   D. The narrator's setting is real, whereas the setting of Waipuo's tale is imaginary.

___ 9. What does Waipuo in "Water Names" say about the family's ancestors?
   A. They rose to the ranks of the nobility.
   B. They were survivors who had the spirit of the river in them.
   C. They successfully resisted foreign invasion of their territory.
   D. Through ambition and hard work, they became very wealthy.

___ 10. How did Waipuo in "Water Names" learn the tale she tells her granddaughters?
   A. She read the tale in a book of family memoirs.
   B. She heard the tale directly from Wen Zhiqing.
   C. Her own grandmother told her the tale.
   D. She read the tale in an old chronicle of medieval China.

___ 11. According to "Water Names," how did Wen Zhiqing catch fish?
   A. with a fishing pole
   B. with nets
   C. with a trained cormorant
   D. with a harpoon

___ 12. In "Water Names," what does Wen Zhiqing's daughter's attitude toward the day's catch suggest?
   A. She is easy-going and carefree.
   B. She always wants more.
   C. She feels guilty about killing fish.
   D. She is lazy and indifferent.

___ 13. In "Water Names," when Wen Zhiqing's daughter looks into the river, who or what sees her face?
   A. the Emperor
   B. Wen Zhiqing
   C. the spirit of a drowned young man
   D. two of the fishermen

___ 14. In "Water Names," what does Wen Zhiqing discover inside the large fish?
   A. a handwritten message
   B. a pearl ring
   C. a gold coin
   D. a silver chain

___ 15. In "Water Names," what kind of conflict does Wen Zhiqing's daughter experience?
   A. a struggle against traditional values
   B. a conflict between her mother and her father
   C. a conflict between desire for adventure and sorrow at leaving her family
   D. a conflict between listening to her grandmother and teasing her sisters

___ 16. In "Water Names," why does Wen Zhiqing forbid his daughter to sit by the water?
   A. He does not want her to marry the prince.
   B. He is afraid that she will become ill from the chilly night air.
   C. He is punishing her for her prior disobedience.
   D. He is afraid that her imagination will cause her harm.

___ 17. What probably happens to the beautiful girl we hear about in "Water Names"?
   A. She is swept away in a terrible flood.
   B. She moves away to live in Nanjing.
   C. She marries another young man, chosen by her father.
   D. She dies of a mysterious disease.

___ 18. In "Water Names," what can you infer about Waipuo from the narrator's descriptive details about her?
   A. Waipuo believes that Wen Zhiqing's daughter deserved to die.
   B. Waipuo identifies somewhat with Wen Zhiqing's daughter.
   C. Waipuo is skeptical about some of the details in the story.
   D. Waipuo becomes impatient when children ask too many questions.

___ 19. Which universal theme does "Water Names" address most directly?
   A. Following our desires can sometimes lead to trouble.
   B. To live life fully, we must understand our roots.
   C. People cannot afford to become prisoners of the past.
   D. Reality is more to be trusted than imagination.

___ 20. Which of the following words best describes the tone of Waipuo's story about Wen Zhiqing's daughter?
   A. skeptical
   B. exaggerated
   C. mysterious
   D. sympathetic

Essay

21. Two striking personalities emerge in "Water Names": the narrator's grandmother, Waipuo, and Wen Zhiqing's daughter, who disappeared long ago. In an essay, compare and contrast Waipuo and Wen Zhiqing's daughter. Support your main idea with specific references to the text.

22. "Water Names" is structured as a tale-within-a-tale. The inner tale about Wen Zhiqing's daughter dominates. What aspects of that tale make it especially suitable for the oral tradition? To answer, write a brief essay in which you tell how the tale's setting, plot, character, and theme appeal to listeners such as the narrator and her sisters. Support your main idea with references to the text.

23. Theme is a central idea, message, or insight that is revealed in a story. A universal theme is a message noticeable in stories of different cultures and time periods. In her comments on "Water Names," the author Lan Samantha Chang has remarked that two important themes in the story concern displacement and the nature of desire. In an essay, discuss how each of these themes comes up in the selection. End your essay by stating whether you consider these themes universal and why or why not.

Unit 6: Themes in American Stories
Part 1 Concept Map

Reading Skills and Strategies:
Summarize

Academic Vocabulary words you can use to discuss making predictions

You can **summarize**

by

rereading to identify main events or ideas

and by

using graphics to organize major events or ideas

(demonstrated in this selection)
Selection name: _____

(demonstrated in this selection)
Selection name: _____

Literary Analysis:
Themes in American Stories

The American Folk Tradition in Print

has its own

mythology

and

dialects

Basic Elements of the American Folk Tradition
• Themes
• Heroes and heroines
• Story telling techniques

The American Folk Tradition in Print
• Myths
• Fables
• Tall Tales
• Epics

Comparing Literary Works:
Heroic Characters

can be

real

fictional

(demonstrated in these selections)
Selection names:
1.
2.

Reading Informational Materials:
Reviews

You can learn to recognize and summarize the **author's message**

by

paying attention to the adjectives he or she uses to describe the book

(demonstrated in this selection)
Selection name: _____

Part 1 Student Log

Complete this chart to track your assignments.

Writing	Extend Your Learning	Writing Workshop	Other Assignments

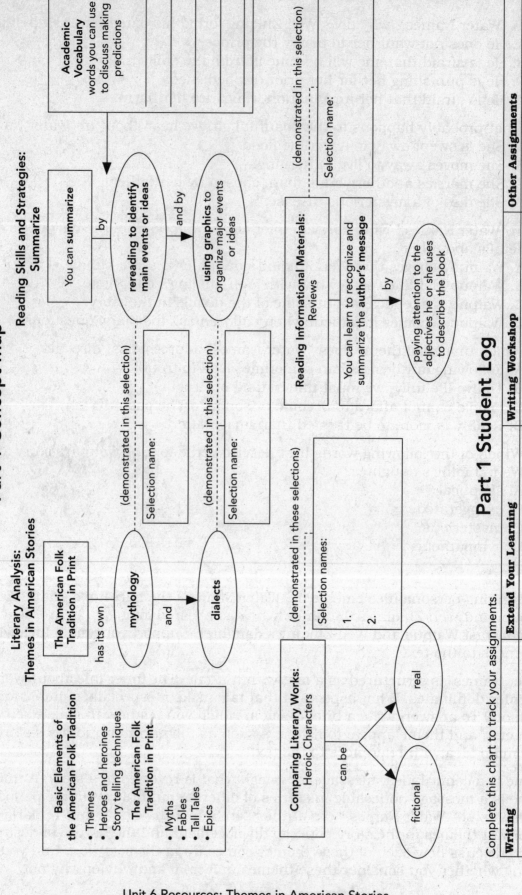

Unit 6: Themes in American Stories
Part 1 Diagnostic Test 11

MULTIPLE CHOICE

Read the selection. Then, answer the questions.

Alexander Graham Bell's invention of the telephone grew out of observing the trials of communication for his mother and wife, both of whom were deaf. Growing up, the needs of the deaf were part of his everyday life. His father taught deaf students and his mother lived the challenges of the deaf. Many people attempted to speak to her through a tube in her ear. Bell had a theory that vibrations from his voice would be a better way to communicate with her. He tested his idea by getting close to her forehead and speaking to her in low, deep tones. It is not clear how successful he was, however, each experience strengthened his inward resolve to understand sound transmission.

As an adult, Bell began teaching at a school for the deaf. There, he met Mabel Hubbard, a student he would later marry. Wanting to help his wife, mother, and others to communicate better, he was determined to continue his studies of the ear and his experiments with sound. In 1875, he successfully transmitted the first sounds over a wire, and in 1876, he invented the telephone. And so the telephone was born from a world of silence.

1. What inspired Bell to investigate how sound is transmitted?
   A. his fascination with the use of wires and tubes
   B. his mother's and wife's constant urging
   C. his father's devotion to teaching the deaf
   D. his desire to help deaf people communicate

2. How did most people try to speak to Bell's mother?
   A. with sign language
   B. by shouting very loudly
   C. through a tube in her ear
   D. by getting close to her forehead

3. The selection states that it is unclear how successful Bell's experiments were with using vibrations to speak to his mother. Based on the information in the selection, what is the most likely explanation for this?
   A. His method was not scientific and his findings could not be measured.
   B. His mother became frustrated and angry at his efforts.
   C. He lost interest in his experiments with how sound is transmitted and heard.
   D. His experiments were a failure, so he was too embarrassed to discuss them.

4. Which of the following most likely motivated Bell to teach at a school for the deaf?
   A. his father's career teaching deaf students
   B. his desire to test his inventions on deaf people
   C. his belief that he would meet his wife there
   D. his unsuccessful experiments with his mother

5. What effect did teaching at a school for the deaf have on Bell?

A. He lost interest in his ideas about sound vibrations and transmitting sound with wires.

B. He became even more determined to learn about how sound is transmitted and heard.

C. He despaired of meeting a woman who could understand his passion for studying sound.

D. He began to pity deaf people and think that there was no way to help them communicate.

6. How did Bell meet his wife?

A. His mother introduced Mabel Hubbard to her son.

B. His father once taught Mabel at a school for the deaf.

C. She was a fellow scientist, also trying to invent a telephone.

D. She was a student at the school for the deaf where he taught.

7. What is the main idea of this selection?

A. Alexander Graham Bell invented the telephone in 1876.

B. A young Bell began experimenting with the idea that deaf people might be able to hear the vibrations of a low voice.

C. As an adult, Bell began teaching at a school for the deaf.

D. Bell's observations of the struggles of deaf people to communicate made him want to learn how sound is transmitted and heard.

Read the selection. Then, answer the questions.

The largest and most famous carnival in the United States is the colossal Mardi Gras celebration held every year in New Orleans. Each year, tourists flock from all over the country to view amazing floats and listen to lively marching bands. Men and women in fantastic costumes balance on the highest tier of multi-level floats and shower the crowd below with colorful beads and trinkets. It is truly a sight to see!

Those who prefer quiet celebrations, however, should stay away. The noise level at Mardi Gras can be excessive, and the crowds that line the parade route tend to get rowdy. The local police are kept very busy trying to keep the public safe during Mardi Gras season.

After the parade, the party continues at fancy costume balls decorated in the official colors of the carnival: purple, which stands for justice; green, which stands for faith; and gold, which stands for power. While most tourists think of Mardi Gras as just an excuse to enjoy a party, some local people continue to honor the customs and traditions that reflect the carnival's ancient origins as a religious festival. Either way, everyone has a good time at Mardi Gras.

8. Mardi Gras is considered to be which of the following?

A. a modest parade

B. a religious festival

C. a colossal party

D. a violent demonstration

9. Which of the following is presented in the selection as a problem of Mardi Gras?

A. The level of noise and that people tend to get rowdy.

B. Police work hard to ensure public safety.

C. Parade participants throw beads to the crowd.

D. There are fancy costume balls after the parade.

10. What are the official colors of Mardi Gras?
   A. blue, red, and green
   B. green, yellow, and silver
   C. purple, green, and gold
   D. purple, red, and orange

11. What does the color green represent at Mardi Gras?
   A. justice
   B. faith
   C. power
   D. tradition

12. According to the selection, what happens after the Mardi Gras parade?
   A. People throw beads.
   B. The tourists all go home.
   C. There is a religious festival.
   D. There are fancy costume balls.

13. What is the origin of Mardi Gras?
   A. It was once a religious festival.
   B. It was once just a small parade that grew to what it is today.
   C. It is an excuse to have a party.
   D. It was invented by the city of New Orleans as a tourist attraction.

14. Which details from the selection most clearly indicates that the writer has probably been to Mardi Gras?
   A. It is truly a sight to see!
   B. Each year, tourists flock from all over the country to view amazing floats and listen to lively marching bands.
   C. People have a good time at Mardi Gras.
   D. Some local people continue to honor the customs and traditions that reflect the carnival's ancient origins.

15. What is the main idea of this selection?
   A. Mardi Gras participants wear costumes and throw beads.
   B. There is a huge parade at Mardi Gras, which tourists enjoy.
   C. Crowds get very loud and rowdy at the Mardi Gras celebration.
   D. Mardi Gras is a huge celebration held in New Orleans each year.

Vocabulary Warm-up Word Lists

Study these words in dialect from "Why the Waves Have Whitecaps." Then, complete the activities.

Word List A

Ah *pron.* I
Ah don't want to have to tell you again!

ast *v.* asked
Your mother has ast you three times to clean your room.

'bout *prep.* about
Dan told me 'bout your plans to go hiking tomorrow.

de *art.* the
After de bad day you had, you must have gone home and cried.

dem or 'em *pron.* them
Did you see dem shopping last night?
Can you take 'em out to eat with you?

git *v.* get
Did you git lots of presents for your birthday?

mo' *adj.* more
Jenny has mo' clothes than any other girl we know.

tole *v.* told
Dad tole you to call home if you were going to be late.

Word List B

chillun *n.* children
Look at all the chillun running around on the school playground.

dat's *contraction* that's or that is
I believe dat's why our weather has been so much warmer this year.

kin *v.* can
Kin we have more than one serving of mashed potatoes?

sho *adj.* sure
Are you sho this is the right way to go to Suzie's house?

squinch *v.* quench
That new sports drink can really squinch your thirst.

'tain't *contraction* there isn't or there is not
Uncle Scott says 'tain't a reason in the world for you to worry.

useter *v.* used to
The choir useter practice every Thursday afternoon for three hours.

wese *pron.* we are
Where did you say wese going for summer vacation?

"Why the Waves Have Whitecaps" by Zora Neale Hurston
Vocabulary Warm-up Exercises

Exercise A *Fill in each blank in the paragraph below with the correct word to replace the dialect word from Word List A.*

Every winter my Aunt Sylvia calls to tell us [**1: 'bout**] _____ the

wonderful Florida weather. "We went walking barefoot on [**2: de**] _____

beach yesterday," she might say. My brothers visited her last year, but

they did not take my sisters or me with [**3: 'em**] _____. We

[**4: ast**] _____ to go [**5: mo'**] _____ than a hundred

times. Mama [**6: tole**] _____ us we were too young. Anyway,

[**7: Ah**] _____ am just waiting for that phone call this year. In Atlanta,

people say we will not [**8: git**] _____ any cold weather for two more

weeks. When Aunt Sylvia calls, we are ready to talk about wearing shorts and T-shirts!

Exercise B *A dialect word is underlined in each question. Write an answer to the question, using your own words in place of the dialect word.*

1. Didn't you <u>useter</u> ride the bus to school?
   _____

2. Whose <u>chillun</u> would you like to baby-sit?
   _____

3. What makes you so <u>sho</u> that your best friend likes you?
   _____

4. Do you agree that <u>'tain't</u> ever a good reason for saying bad things about others?
   _____

5. <u>Kin</u> you ever really relax and just do nothing?
   _____

6. Would you say that as Americans <u>wese</u> the luckiest people in the world?
   _____

7. What drink do you crave when you really want to <u>squinch</u> your thirst?
   _____

8. What do you own <u>dat's</u> most valuable to you?
   _____

"Why the Waves Have Whitecaps" by Zora Neale Hurston

Reading Warm-up A

Read the following passage. Pay special attention to the underlined words. Then, read it again, and complete the activities. Use a separate sheet of paper for your written answers.

Dialect is spoken language that is special to a certain part of the country. For example, some people in the southern United States have unique ways of talking.

For a dialect to develop, two things must be true. First, people have to live together in a small area. Second, this group must be separate from other groups.

Sometimes the way of talking relates to how words are pronounced. For example, *th* at the beginning of words can be replaced by *d*. Instead of *the*, people might say <u>de</u>. A sentence with a bunch of *th-* words might sound like this:

On de dird Dursday of de month, we always eat dinner together, so we can see <u>dem</u>.

Ending sounds also change—for example, *asked* is said <u>ast</u> in some parts of the South.

Other ways of talking in dialect involve dropping sounds from words. Instead of saying *more*, some people say <u>mo'</u>. Speakers also drop the first sounds of words, saying <u>'bout</u> instead of *about*, for example. To describe people who are needy, some might say:

Those po' people need mo' money, and I'm talkin' 'bout givin' it to all of 'em right now!

Sometimes, vowel sounds are stretched out or changed in dialects. Someone with a drawl, in which sounds are stretched out and changed, says <u>Ah</u> instead of *I*, for example. On the other hand, the short *i* sound is very popular in some places. Instead of *get*, people say <u>git</u>. So, you might hear a woman call her pet like this:

Binji, Ah have ast you dree times to git in de house. Come on now!

If all of this seems confusing, just remember that lots of older people cannot understand your Internet chat dialect. That's right, no one ever <u>tole</u> them that *lol* means "laugh out loud" and not "lots of love."

1. Look at the dialect sentence in dark type with *dem* in it. Underline the other words using *d* for *th*. Then, list them with the standard English words beside them.

2. Find and circle <u>ast</u>. What does it mean in standard English? Now, change the word *risked* to dialect. Write a sentence using it.

3. Underline the words with dropped sounds in the sentence in dark type with <u>mo'</u> and <u>'bout</u>. Then, list the words with the standard English words beside them.

4. Find and circle <u>Ah</u>. Notice how *I* changes to *Ah* in dialect. Write a sentence in dialect using as many long *i* words as you can. Read it aloud to a friend.

5. In an area where *get* is said *git*, how would you pronounce *pen*? Explain.

6. Rewrite the dialect sentence in which the woman calls her pet, using standard English.

7. Underline the dialect word in the last paragraph. What word does it represent in standard English?

"Why the Waves Have Whitecaps" by Zora Neale Hurston

Reading Warm-up B

Read the following passage. Pay special attention to the underlined words. Then, read it again, and complete the activities. Use a separate sheet of paper for your written answers.

Movie stars do lots of things to make us believe they are the people whose roles they play. They lose or gain weight, endure hours of makeup sessions every day, and study the facts about the people, times, and places in their movies. Also, stars often have to learn the dialect, or way of speaking, of their characters. Sometimes, they must get coaching in order to do this well.

For an actor or actress raised to speak standard English, you can imagine how hard it would be to constantly use 'tain't, for instance. After all, didn't most of us learn in third grade that *ain't* isn't a real word? Imagine, too, how awkward it might feel to say <u>wese</u>, short for *we is*, when the standard English is *we are*.

Part of the training that stars receive helps them to become more knowledgeable about how and why the dialect developed and the people who use it. Actors, thus, learn to appreciate the history and customs behind that way of speaking. With this understanding, negative judgments about how people speak can be avoided.

In dialect, there are also those words that just don't "sound right." What in the world does <u>chillun</u> mean? For modern stars in Los Angeles, it sounds like what you do when you are relaxing! What about <u>squinch</u>? Is that what happens when you close your eyes tightly because you have an itch? You can see why training and explanations are so important if stars are to use dialect correctly and be convincing.

So, if you <u>useter</u> think movie stars have an easy life, remember how tough their training really is. They <u>sho</u> don't start speaking in a southern dialect overnight. It <u>kin</u> take months of preparation. Really, if a star has to become incredibly fit, lose twenty pounds, change hairstyles, dress in weird clothes, and learn a whole new dialect, <u>dat's</u> worth millions of dollar, *ain't* it?

1. Find and circle 'tain't. Explain what the writer is trying to point out by putting *ain't* and *isn't* next to each other when talking about *'tain't*.

2. Circle the words that are the correct replacements for <u>wese</u>. Explain why using *we is* would not make most teachers happy.

3. Find and circle <u>chillun</u> in the passage. What might stars think *chillun* means? Explain what *chillun* really means.

4. Underline the question that the writer asks to try to define <u>squinch</u>. Then, explain what *squinch* really means.

5. Circle the four dialect words that are underlined in the last paragraph. List them and write the standard English words beside them. Then, use all four dialect words in a short paragraph.

Name _____ Date _____

"Why the Waves Have Whitecaps" by Zora Neale Hurston
Reading: Create a Summary

A **summary** is a short statement that presents the main points in a piece of writing. Summarizing helps you focus on the most important information and remember it better. You also may need to summarize a work as part of your discussion of it.

Follow this strategy when you summarize a work that tells a story:

- Reread the work to identify the main events.
- Restate these events in complete sentences.
- Put the sentences in chronological order.
- Cross out any minor details that do not seem important enough to include.
- Be sure that your sentences mention all the major points, including the main characters and settings.
- Revise your sentences so that they use as few words as possible.

DIRECTIONS: *Follow the numbered instructions to revise this paragraph into a good summary of "Why the Waves Have Whitecaps."*

The wind and the water are both characters. They used to speak proudly and boastfully about their children. Mrs. Wind said one thing and Mrs. Water said another. Mrs. Water got so sick and tired of hearing about Mrs. Wind's children that one day, when the children came to drink her water, she drowned them. When Mrs. Wind went to look for her children, Mrs. Water said she had not seen them. Mrs. Wind searched high and low. Mrs. Wind passed over the water calling for her children. Whitecaps came to the top. _____

_____

1. Add a key detail to the first sentence.
2. Replace the phrase "speak proudly and boastfully" with a single word.
3. Remove two unnecessary words from the fourth sentence.
4. Cross out the two sentences that most clearly do not belong in the summary.
5. Reword the last two sentences to make the relationship between them clear.
6. On the lines at the end, add a sentence that makes clear what the myth explains.

Name _____ Date _____

"Why the Waves Have Whitecaps" by Zora Neale Hurston
Literary Analysis: Myth

A **myth** is an ancient tale that presents the beliefs or customs of a culture or people. Most myths try to explain an aspect of nature, history, or human behavior. They often feature supernatural creatures like gods and goddesses or contain animals or forces of nature that display human qualities. "Why the Waves Have Whitecaps" is Zora Neale Hurston's retelling of an African American myth.

DIRECTIONS: *Answer these questions about the retold myth "Why the Waves Have Whitecaps."*

1. What does the myth try to explain?

   _____

2. Sum up the explanation in three or four sentences.

   _____

   _____

   _____

   _____

3. What supernatural creatures, humanlike animals, or forces of nature does the myth feature as characters?

   _____

4. What human qualities do these characters display?

   _____

   _____

   _____

5. What does the myth suggest about the role of nature in African American life in times past? Explain.

   _____

   _____

   _____

6. What else does the myth suggest about African American life?

   _____

   _____

   _____

Name _____ Date _____

"Why the Waves Have Whitecaps" by Zora Neale Hurston
Vocabulary Builder

To make "Why the Waves Have Whitecaps" seem like authentic oral storytelling, Hurston tells it in African American dialect. **Dialect** is the vocabulary and grammar used in a particular region or by a particular group. Because it differs from **standard English,** the most widely known and accepted form of the language, it may contain terms that are puzzling at first. To understand a puzzling dialect term, follow these steps:

- Consider whether it might mean the same as a more familiar word or phrase that it sounds like.
- Use its position in a sentence to help you determine what part of speech it might be.
- Look for other clues about the term in its **context,** or surrounding words.
- Once you guess the meaning, replace the term with your guess to see if it makes sense.

For example, in the sentence "They useter talk together a whole heap," you can figure out that *useter* probably means "used to" because it sounds like those words, its position in the sentence suggests that it functions as a verb, and "used to" makes sense in the context.

A. DIRECTIONS: *Use the sound, position, and other context clues to figure out the meaning of each underlined dialect term. Then, circle the letter of the correct meaning.*

1. De wind is a woman, and de water is a woman too.
   A. day   B. did   C. the   D. deed
2. They was jus' like all lady people. They loved to talk about their chillun, and brag on 'em.
   A. chill out   B. child   C. children   D. killing
3. One day a whole passle of her chillun come to Mrs. Wind. . . .
   A. large group   B. small coin   C. pass out   D. people
4. "Mama, wese thirsty. Kin we go git us a cool drink of water?"
   A. I am   B. we are   C. wheeze   D. become
5. When them chillun went to squinch they thirst Mrs. Water grabbed 'em all. . . .
   A. squint   B. spinach   C. crunch   D. quench

B. DIRECTIONS: *Rewrite this dialect passage in standard English.*

"Oh, but Ah got mo' different chilluns than anybody in de world. They flies, they walks, they swims, they sings, they talks, they cries. They got all de colors from de sun. Lawd, my chillun sho is a pleasure. 'Tain't nobody got no babies like mine."

_____

_____

_____

_____

"Why the Waves Have Whitecaps" by Zora Neale Hurston
Support for Writing a Myth

Use the chart below to help you gather details for the myth you will create. For statements by characters, use dialect, idioms, and humor. They will make the myth seem more authentic.

Subject (Natural Feature or Event to Be Explained)	
Main Characters	
Setting (Time and Place)	
Main Events of the Myth	
Statements by Characters (include Dialect, Idioms, and Humor)	

"Why the Waves Have Whitecaps" by Zora Neale Hurston
Support for Extend Your Learning

Research and Technology

African and African American cultures include many stories that explain natural events such as a drought or a flood. First, look up a natural event in print or electronic sources that specialize in African or African American cultures. Use the chart below to list the main points of one African or African American myth. Second, look up and list the main points of a scientific explanation for the same event.

Natural Event: _____	
Explanation From an African or African American Myth	**Explanation From Science**

Listening and Speaking

Use this chart to record what your research shows you about cultural traditions of African Americans and the influence of other cultures on African Americans. You can investigate African American wedding customs, holidays, or another tradition.

Source	
Author (if known)	
Traditional beliefs that influence African American culture today	
Outside influences on African American culture today	

"Why the Waves Have Whitecaps" by Zora Neale Hurston

Enrichment: Ocean Waves

The myth that Hurston retells does have a parallel in scientific fact: Wind does, indeed, cause waves to have whitecaps. When wind hits the water, the water is pushed into waves. The following diagram shows the main characteristics of waves.

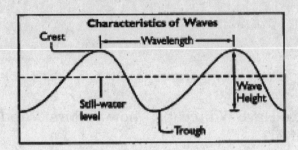

As the wind blows across the surface of the water, little ripples begin to form. When the wind gets stronger, the ripples become larger waves. The size of the wave is determined by how fast the wind is blowing, the length of time the wind blows, and the distance the wind blows over the water. As each of these factors increases, the height of the wave increases. Some waves can become huge. In 1933, for example, the United States Navy measured a surface wave higher than a ten-story building!

DIRECTIONS: *Use the diagram and the information above to answer these questions.*

1. What is the high spot of a wave called? _____

2. What is the low spot of a wave called? _____

3. What is the distance between two crests (or two troughs) called? _____

4. What is the distance from the trough to the crest called? _____

5. What do you think would happen if wind came from more than one direction at once?
_____

6. What do you think would happen to a boat on water that had small waves?
_____

7. What would happen to a boat on water in which the waves got bigger and bigger?
_____
_____

"Why the Waves Have Whitecaps" by Zora Neale Hurston
Selection Test A

Critical Reading *Identify the letter of the choice that best answers the question.*

____ 1. According to "Why the Waves Have Whitecaps," what are the wind and the water?
  A. women
  B. sisters
  C. neighbors
  D. all of the above

____ 2. In "Why the Waves Have Whitecaps," how do Mrs. Wind and Mrs. Water feel about their children?
  A. proud
  B. ashamed
  C. disappointed
  D. angry

____ 3. In "Why the Waves Have Whitecaps," what does Mrs. Water do when Mrs. Wind's children come for a drink?
  A. She kidnaps them.
  B. She gives them a drink.
  C. She poisons the water.
  D. She drowns them.

____ 4. In "Why the Waves Have Whitecaps," what happens when Mrs. Wind comes looking for her children?
  A. Mrs. Water hides.
  B. Mrs. Water pretends that she has not seen the children.
  C. Mrs. Water confesses to having killed the children.
  D. Mrs. Water brags about her own children.

____ 5. Which event would you be most likely to include in a summary of "Why the Waves Have Whitecaps"?
  A. Mrs. Wind used to go down to the water to patch and crochet.
  B. Mrs. Wind says, "Ah got de biggest and de littlest in de world."
  C. Mrs. Wind bragged about her children so much that Mrs. Water began to hate them.
  D. Mrs. Water's children asked if they could go get a drink.

___ 6. Which event would you be *least* likely to include in a summary of "Why the Waves Have Whitecaps"?

   A. Mrs. Wind and Mrs. Water bragged about their children.

   B. Mrs. Wind said that she had more children than anybody in the world.

   C. Mrs. Water drowned Mrs. Wind's children.

   D. Whitecaps form as Mrs. Wind passes over the water looking for her children.

___ 7. What is the main purpose of the myth about Mrs. Wind and Mrs. Water?

   A. to help people understand human nature

   B. to show the danger of choppy waters

   C. to explain a natural occurrence

   D. to teach right from wrong

___ 8. Which characteristic of myths applies to "Why the Waves Have Whitecaps"?

   A. A myth often features gods and goddesses.

   B. A myth is based on scientific fact.

   C. A myth often features forces of nature that act like human beings.

   D. all of the above

Vocabulary and Grammar

___ 9. Which word means the opposite of *organized*?

   A. organization

   B. disorganized

   C. extract

   D. sequence

___ 10. Which sentence is a compound sentence?

   A. When the children went for a drink, Mrs. Water drowned them.

   B. The children wanted a drink, but Mrs. Water drowned them.

   C. The children went for a drink and drowned in the water.

   D. When the children went for a drink, Mrs. Water drowned them because she hated them.

Essay

11. In a short essay, summarize the myth about Mrs. Wind and Mrs. Water. Tell what aspect of nature the myth explains, and give the important details of that explanation.

"Why the Waves Have Whitecaps" by Zora Neale Hurston
Selection Test B

Critical Reading *Identify the letter of the choice that best completes the statement or answers the question.*

____ 1. Which phrase best characterizes the bragging that Mrs. Wind and Mrs. Water do in "Why the Waves Have Whitecaps"?
A. typical of many parents
B. highly unusual in a parent
C. deeply philosophical
D. devious and dishonest

____ 2. In "Why the Waves Have Whitecaps," what motivates Mrs. Wind and Mrs. Water to brag about their children?
A. pride and envy
B. greed and ambition
C. desire for fame
D. all the above

____ 3. In "Why the Waves Have Whitecaps," who are the children Mrs. Water describes in this passage?

Ah got de biggest and de littlest in de world. All kinds of chillun. Every color in de world, and every shape!

A. all the living things of Earth
B. the different races of human beings
C. creatures and plants that live in the sea
D. African American children

____ 4. Which statement best summarizes what happens to Mrs. Wind's children in "Why the Waves Have Whitecaps"?
A. The children are thirsty and long for a cool drink.
B. The children are thirsty. They want a cool drink. They go for it. Mrs. Water drowns them.
C. When the children go for a drink, Mrs. Water drowns them.
D. The children drown before they can get a cool drink of water. It is all Mrs. Water's fault.

____ 5. In "Why the Waves Have Whitecaps," why does Mrs. Water drown Mrs. Wind's children?
A. as a warning to other children
B. to protect her own children
C. to hurt Mrs. Wind for bragging so much
D. to demonstrate her power

____ 6. Which word best describes the women in "Why the Waves Have Whitecaps"?
A. shy
B. competitive
C. uncaring
D. humble

___ 7. Which statement best summarizes Mrs. Wind's attitude regarding her children in "Why the Waves Have Whitecaps"?
   A. She is proud of their achievements and shattered when they disappear.
   B. She loves her children, but she recognizes their shortcomings as well as their strengths.
   C. She neglects her children until they disappear, and then she realizes what she has lost.
   D. She resents the demands of her children because she would rather talk with Mrs. Water.

___ 8. What do the events and details in "Why the Waves Have Whitecaps" suggest about the relationship of African Americans to nature in past times?
   A. African Americans lived close to nature and sought to explain its mysteries.
   B. African Americans lived in large cities and had little understanding of nature.
   C. African Americans were more interested in human relationships than they were in nature.
   D. African Americans were deeply concerned about human destruction of nature.

___ 9. In "Why the Waves Have Whitecaps," what is the effect of the African American dialect?
   A. It makes the characters seem like everyday people.
   B. It helps capture the flavor of oral storytelling.
   C. It stresses the African American origins of the myth.
   D. all of the above

Vocabulary and Grammar

___ 10. In which sentence is the underlined word used correctly?
   A. To build muscle, it is <u>essential</u> to exercise.
   B. Do not let minor worries <u>extract</u> you from your main purpose.
   C. After she gave blood, she felt dizzy and <u>organized</u>.
   D. A good filing system is completely <u>disorganized</u>.

___ 11. What type of sentence is this statement from "Why the Waves Have Whitecaps"?
   When you see a storm on de water, it's de wind and de water fightin' over dem chillun.
   A. simple
   B. compound
   C. complex
   D. compound-complex

Essay

12. In a brief essay, explain how Mrs. Water and Mrs. Wind are like and unlike everyday people. First, examine the everyday human qualities, attitudes, and behavior that they display. Then, discuss how their behavior is unlike that of human beings.

13. Explain why "Why the Waves Have Whitecaps" is a myth. Identify at least three characteristics of myths, and show how this particular myth illustrates those characteristics.

Vocabulary Warm-up Word Lists

Study these words from "Coyote Steals the Sun and Moon." Then, complete the activities.

Word List A

chattering [CHAT uhr ing] *v.* knocking together
  My teeth started <u>chattering</u> as the cold wind blew harder and harder.

coyote [kye OH tee] *n.* a small, wild dog that lives in the West.
  The man was alarmed when he heard the <u>coyote</u> howling.

curiosity [kyoor ee AHS uh tee] *n.* the desire to know something
  Steve's <u>curiosity</u> about how hockey began led him to the library.

eagle [EE guhl] *n.* a large bird that feeds on small animals
  An <u>eagle</u> has a hooked beak and long, powerful wings.

lend [LEND] *v.* to give something for just a short time
  Carly hoped her brother would <u>lend</u> her his CD player.

nudged [NUJD] *v.* pushed or poked gently
  My partner <u>nudged</u> me in the ribs with his elbow to get my attention.

panting [PANT ing] *v.* breathing quickly and loudly
  After rushing up the stairs, I was <u>panting</u> and starting to sweat.

produce [pruh DOOS] *v.* to make something happen
  Does Ms. Conklin actually think her jokes will <u>produce</u> laughter?

Word List B

delayed [di LAYD] *v.* made someone or something late
  In busy cities, people often are <u>delayed</u> by traffic.

lagged [LAGD] *v.* moved more slowly than others
  After a poor start, Tim <u>lagged</u> behind the other racers.

melons [MEL uhnz] *n.* large, juicy fruits with hard skin and flat seeds
  At our Fourth of July party, we always have lots of sweet <u>melons</u>.

pestering [PES tuhr ing] *n.* the act of bothering someone
  Joe kept <u>pestering</u> his brother to take him the m???.

pueblo [PWEB loh] *n.* a Native American village in the Southwest.
  On our trip to the Grand Canyon, we visited a <u>pueblo</u>.

sacred [SAY krid] *adj.* believed to be holy or deserving great respect
  Some things in nature are considered <u>sacred</u> objects to many people.

shriveled [SHRIV uhld] *v.* dried up; withered
  A raisin is actually nothing more than a grape that has <u>shriveled.</u>

squashes [SKWAHSH ez] *n.* large, firm vegetables with a hard skin
  At the farmer's market, I saw <u>squashes</u> of all colors and sizes.

Name _____ Date _____

Vocabulary Warm-up Exercises

Exercise A *Fill in each blank in the paragraph below with an appropriate word from Word List A. Use each word only once.*

The woman's teeth were [1] _____, not from cold but from fear. She was

lost in the desert. Every time a [2] _____ howled, she became more

scared. She was sorry for her [3] _____, which had led her to explore

something away from the group. She was [4] _____ from the heat, wish-

ing she haken the hat a friend offered to [5] _____ her for the trip. Any-

thing that would [6] _____ shade would be welcome. Then, a shadow fell

on her. Looking up, she saw a huge [7] _____. Its wings gave her shade.

Suddenly she felt as if someone had [8] _____ her and made her turn

east. Within minutes, she spotted her group. The eagle left her as she reached them.

Exercise B *Decide whether each statement below is true or false. Circle T or F, and explain your answers.*

1. People usually peel <u>squashes</u> with their fingers.
   T / F _____

2. A popular tourist spot in Maine is an early American <u>pueblo</u>.
   T / F _____

3. When school buses are <u>delayed</u> on foggy mornings, student riders get to school early.
   T / F _____

4. Plants that have <u>shriveled</u> are commonly seen in areas in which rainfall levels have <u>lagged</u> behind the usual amounts.
   T / F _____

5. People would not find napkins useful when enjoying ripe <u>melons</u>.
   T / F _____

6. The constant barking of a neighbor's dog is something that could be described as a kind of <u>pestering</u>.
   T / F _____

7. A <u>sacred</u> promise is less important than a passing remark that you will do something.
   T / F _____

Name _____ Date _____

"Coyote Steals the Sun and Moon" retold by Richard Erdoes and Alfonso Ortiz
Reading Warm-up A

Read the following passage. Pay special attention to the underlined words. Then, read it again, and complete the activities. Use a separate sheet of paper for your written answers.

When I was small, my mother used to make up stories to tell me. Because I had such a huge underline{curiosity} about all things, she found that books often would not hold my attention. At least, I would interrupt nearly every sentence to ask questions. Sometimes, I even <u>nudged</u> her to get her attention.

So, each night Mom would request that I give her a list of three characters. Then, she would <u>produce</u> a story that featured them. Always, the stories were great, and by the time it ended, I was usually <u>panting</u> with excitement and asking for more. However, Mom's limit was one story per night.

My requested characters were always animals. A favorite was the magnificent <u>eagle</u>. I think Mom liked the eagle as a character, too. She usually talked about its keen eyes, but really meant that the graceful bird had great wisdom. I also often chose the sly <u>coyote</u>. I think Mom usually made this tricky animal the bad guy, but in a humorous way.

I only wish someone had written down Mom's stories because I would love to have been able to <u>lend</u> them to my own children to read today. I've never been a very good oral storyteller. It feels too much like public speaking, a scary situation that usually leaves my teeth <u>chattering</u>. So, I could never tell the stories to others.

Still, I think Mom's art with words probably led me toward my career. As a writer of stories based on myths, I can craft them with carefully selected words. I work alone, with just my imagination and research beside me. The reader I keep in mind is myself as a curious, questioning young boy.

I'm sorry that my readers cannot listen to my mom, inventing clever plots that twist and turn all along the way. How in the world was she so wonderfully creative on the spot?

1. Underline the sentence that describes the boy's <u>curiosity</u>. Then, describe something that brings out your *curiosity*.

2. Underline the words that help to understand <u>nudged</u>. Write a sentence using *nudged*.

3. Circle the word naming what Mom would <u>produce</u>. Then, explain what *produce* means.

4. Underline the words telling when the boy was <u>panting</u>. Explain why *panting* may happen when someone is excited.

5. Circle one word that describes the <u>eagle</u> and one that describes the <u>coyote</u>. Then, write a sentence using a different descriptive word for each animal.

6. Underline the words naming what the writer would like to <u>lend</u>. Then, explain what *lend* means.

7. Circle the two words that name what leaves the writer's teeth <u>chattering</u>. Then, list three times when your teeth have been *chattering*.

"Coyote Steals the Sun and Moon" retold by Richard Erdoes and Alfonso Ortiz
Reading Warm-up B

Read the following passage. Pay special attention to the underlined words. Then, read it again, and complete the activities. Use a separate sheet of paper for your written answers.

Thousands of years ago, people living in hot, dry areas of North America began making homes out of the sand that was all around them. They believed that nature was sacred and often used its gifts for good purposes. The people spread a thick clay or mud mixture over sticks and twigs that they had woven together. The mixture dried hard and made sturdy walls. Inside these walls, the temperature was pleasant. No animals or bugs were able to get through the walls to keep pestering the people.

Later, people began to make bricks out of the mud. They mixed in chopped up plants and then shaped the blend into cubes that dried in the sun. Possibly, early Spanish explorers taught Native Americans to make these adobe bricks, since the Spanish did use them in building their own homes in Spain. Certainly, the Spaniards gave the Native American villages they found the name pueblo.

A pueblo of long ago was not unlike a friendly apartment building today. Many families lived together in homes that were stacked and connected together. The roof of a bottom house was like the front yard of the house above it.

People used ladders to climb from one part of the village to another. At night, the pueblo dwellers put away all ladders, so if you lagged behind everyone else in returning to the village, you might not get back in. No one wanted to be delayed by anything!

Because these ancient peoples were successful farmers, they were able to build permanent homes. While other groups moved from place to place hunting and gathering their food, pueblo dwellers could settle down. They grew corn, beans, and different types of squashes. Some groups also enjoyed sweet melons.

Scientists believe many pueblo dwellers were forced to leave their homes because of a long drought. By A.D. 1300, after twenty-five years of very little rain and crops that had shriveled and died, most pueblos stood empty.

1. Underline the word naming something the people believed was sacred. Explain something that is *sacred* to you.

2. Circle the words naming the two things that did the pestering. Explain how these might have kept up the *pestering*.

3. Circle the word that means the same as pueblo. Then, describe a *pueblo* in your own words.

4. Underline the words describing what might happen if someone lagged behind. Then, explain what *lagged* means.

5. Underline the words that tell who did not want to be delayed. Then, tell about a time you were *delayed*.

6. Circle the words naming other things pueblo dwellers grew besides squashes and melons. Then, write a sentence comparing *squashes* to *melons*.

7. Underline the word that gives a hint to the meaning of shriveled. Then, explain what *shriveled* means.

"Coyote Steals the Sun and Moon" retold by Richard Erdoes and Alfonso Ortiz

Reading: Create a Summary

A **summary** is a short statement that presents the main points in a piece of writing. Summarizing helps you focus on the most important information and remember it better. You also may need to summarize a work as part of your discussion of it.

Follow this strategy when you summarize a work that tells a story:

- Reread the work to identify the main events.
- Restate these events in complete sentences.
- Put the sentences in chronological order.
- Cross out any minor details that do not seem important enough to include.
- Be sure that your sentences mention all the major points, including the main characters and settings.
- Revise your sentences so that they use as few words as possible.

A. DIRECTIONS: *Answer the questions about a summary of "Coyote Steals the Sun and Moon."*

1. Which two characters would be most important to mention in your summary?

   _____   _____

2. What are three settings that should be mentioned in your summary?

   _____   _____   _____

3. Restate two things a character says that should be included in your summary.

   _____

   _____

4. List two things the characters do that should be included in your summary.

   _____

   _____

B. DIRECTIONS: *Based on the guidelines and your answers to items 1–4 above, write a summary of "Coyote Steals the Sun and Moon." Use the space below or a separate sheet of paper.*

   _____

   _____

   _____

   _____

   _____

   _____

"Coyote Steals the Sun and Moon" retold by Richard Erdoes and Alfonso Ortiz

Literary Analysis: Myth

In ancient times, people wondered about the world, just as people do today. Sometimes they told stories to try to explain it. These stories are called myths. A **myth** is an ancient tale that presents the beliefs or customs of a culture. Most myths try to explain an aspect of nature, history, or human behavior. They usually feature supernatural creatures and often contain animals or forces of nature that display human qualities.

You can usually understand a myth better if you know something about the culture that produced it. For example, when you read the Zuñi myth "Coyote Steals the Sun and Moon," it helps to know that the Zuñi are a Native American people from the American Southwest. The myth itself also reveals information about the culture or landscape in which it is set.

DIRECTIONS: *Use this chart to show what "Coyote Steals the Sun and Moon" tells you about Native American people like the Zuñi and their life in the Southwest. For each detail in the left column, list at least one insight it gives you into the culture or setting. The insight from the first detail has been given as an example.*

Detail	Insight
1. Coyote and Eagle hunt rabbits.	• Coyotes and eagles are found in the Southwest. • Southwestern tribes sometimes hunted.
2. Coyote and Eagle come to a village called a pueblo.	
3. The people in the pueblo watch Kachinas do a sacred dance.	
4. Coyote says to Eagle, "You're my chief."	
5. Eagle gives Coyote the box because "if someone asks four times, you'd better give him what he wants."	
6. Peaches, squashes, and melons shrivel up with the cold.	

Name _____ Date _____

Vocabulary Builder

Word List

| sacred | pestering | shriveled | pursuit |

A. DIRECTIONS: *Answer the questions with complete sentences, using each World List word only once and underlining it.*

1. What is one book that many people consider holy?

   _____

   _____

2. What small wrinkled fruit is made by drying grapes in the sun?

   _____

   _____

3. What does a police car do when chasing a criminal?

   _____

   _____

4. How do most people react to being annoyed constantly?

   _____

   _____

B. DIRECTIONS: *Circle the letter of the word that is most nearly* <u>opposite</u> *in meaning to the word in CAPITAL LETTERS.*

1. SACRED:
   A. holy   B. fully   C. sinful   D. greedy
2. PESTERING:
   A. ignoring   B. reducing   C. whispering   D. remembering
3. SHRIVELED:
   A. wrinkled   B. shrunken   C. scary   D. smooth
4. PURSUIT:
   A. race   B. capture   C. search   D. need

Name _____ Date _____

Support for Writing a Myth

Use the chart below to help you gather details for the myth you will create. For statements by the characters, use dialect, idioms, and humor. They will make the myth seem authentic.

Subject (Natural Feature or Event to Be Explained)	
Main Characters	
Setting (Time and Place)	
Main Events of the Myth	
Statements by Characters (include Dialect, Idioms, and Humor)	

"Coyote Steals the Sun and Moon" retold by Richard Erdoes and Alfonso Ortiz
Support for Extend Your Learning

Research and Technology

Native American culture includes many myths that explain natural events such as wind, fire, rain, and the seasons. First, look up the natural event in print or electronic sources that specialize in Native American culture. Use this chart to list the main points of one Native American myth. Second, look up and list the main points of a scientific explanation for the same event.

Natural Event: _____	
Explanation From Native American Myth	**Explanation From Science**

Listening and Speaking

Use this chart to record what your research shows you about a cultural tradition of the Zuñi and the influence of other cultures on the Zuñi. You can investigate the Zuñi tradition of the Snake Dance, the kiva, marriage and divorce, or another tradition.

Source	
Author (if known)	
Traditional beliefs that influence the Zuñi today	
Outside influences on the Zuñi today	

"Coyote Steals the Sun and Moon" retold by Richard Erdoes and Alfonso Ortiz

Enrichment: Coyote the Trickster

Tales of tricks or pranks and those who play them have amused people since the dawn of storytelling. Among Native Americans, the greatest trickster is Coyote. Coyote the Trickster exhibits human qualities. Stories usually tell of his cleverness and foolishness, his delight in mischief, his never-ending appetite, his ability to cheat his enemies, and his reactions when someone else manages to trick him.

An actual coyote is a wild animal with a long pointy nose, pointy ears, and a thick bushy tail. It resembles a small wolf and, like a wolf, is a member of the dog family. Coyotes have a striking cry, a series of high-pitched barks and yodels. Coyotes normally live on prairies and in brushy areas and open woodland. They are very adaptable and can survive in urban areas, living in the margins of highways and other natural corridors. Nighttime hunters, they generally survive on rodents, rabbits, birds, and other small animals, but they also eat insects, fruit, and garbage. Because they sometimes feed on livestock, farmers in the 1800s placed bounties on coyotes, and many were shot, poisoned, and trapped. However, while local populations were sometimes wiped out, coyotes overall survived and flourished. Since the 1950s, some coyotes have even traveled east along the interstate highway system and now live in the Northeast and Southeast.

A. DIRECTIONS: *Use the information above to help you answer these questions.*

1. Why do you think trickster tales have such widespread appeal?

_____

_____

_____

_____

2. Why do you think Native Americans chose to portray coyotes as tricksters?

_____

_____

_____

B. DIRECTIONS: *What animal would you choose to star in trickster stories? Why?*

_____

_____

_____

_____

"Why the Waves Have Whitecaps" by Zora Neale Hurston
"Coyote Steals the Sun and Moon" retold by Richard Erdoes and Alfonso Ortiz

Build Language Skills: Vocabulary

The Prefix *dis-*

The prefix *dis-* means "not" or "the opposite of." It is often used to form antonyms, words that mean the opposite of other words. For example, *organized* means "arranged in logical order." When you add the prefix *dis-*, you get *disorganized*, which means "not arranged in logical order."

A. DIRECTIONS: *Rewrite each sentence so that it means the opposite of the original sentence by adding the prefix* dis- *to one of the words in the original sentence. You will also have to change other words or the order of the words so that the new sentence makes sense.*

Original sentence: An honest person tells the truth.
Sentence with opposite meaning: A *dishonest* person tells lies.

1. Janis nodded her head to show that she agreed.

_____

2. The director was pleased with the fine performances.

_____

3. The ferry is continuing operation, so you can take it next month.

_____

4. She mounted the horse and rode off.

_____

5. The people bowed and curtsied respectfully when the king passed.

_____

B. DIRECTIONS: *Fill in the blanks using each Word List word only once.*

Word List

essential	extract	organized	disorganized	sequence

1. A good secretary keeps the office files _____.
2. Good swimming skills are _____ if you want to be a lifeguard.
3. The phone book puts name in an alphabetical _____.
4. It is hard to find things on a/an _____ desktop.
5. Can you _____ blue dye from indigo plants?

"Why the Waves Have Whitecaps" by Zora Neale Hurston
"Coyote Steals the Sun and Moon" retold by Richard Erdoes and Alfonso Ortiz

Build Language Skills: Grammar

Sentence Structures

A **clause** is a group of words with at least one subject (*S*) and one verb (*V*). An **independent clause** can stand on its own as a sentence; a **subordinate clause** cannot.

Independent Clauses	Subordinate Clauses
S V The school bell rang.	S V When the school bell rang
S S V V The boys and girls shouted and cheered.	S S V V As the boys and girls shouted and cheered

Sentences are classified by their clauses. A **simple sentence** includes one independent clause:

    The school bell rang.   The boys and girls shouted and cheered.

A **compound sentence** has two or more independent clauses joined by a comma (or commas) and a coordinating conjunction (*and, or, but, so, nor, for,* or *yet*) or by a semicolon. In these examples, each independent clause is underlined.

    The school bell rang, *but* class continued. The school bell rang; class continued.

A **complex sentence** has one independent clause (indicated by one underline) and one or more subordinate clauses (indicated by a double underline).

    When the school bell rang, the children raced to the bus that stood by the curb.

A **compound-complex** sentence has at least two independent clauses and at least one subordinate clause.

    When the clock chimed three, the school bell rang, and the children raced to the bus.

A. PRACTICE: *Underline each independent clause once and each subordinate clause twice. Label the* sentence *simple, compound, complex, or compound-complex.*

_____ 1. The Northwest is damp and rainy, but the Southwest is dry.

_____ 2. When it rains, many desert flowers bloom.

B. Writing Application: *Rewrite the sentences as instructed.*

1. The beach traffic is usually heavy in summer. This weekend was an exception. (Combine into a compound sentence.) _____

_____

2. I stood on the beach. The waves rushed to shore. The seagulls flew overhead. (Combine into a compound-complex sentence.) _____

_____

"Coyote Steals the Sun and Moon" retold by Richard Erdoes and Alfonso Ortiz

Selection Test A

Critical Reading *Identify the letter of the choice that best answers the question.*

_____ 1. In "Coyote Steals the Sun and Moon," why does Coyote ask Eagle to hunt with him?
   A. Eagle is a better hunter, and Coyote wants more meat.
   B. Eagle can provide him with tasty insects to eat.
   C. Coyote wants to fatten Eagle up to be eaten later.
   D. Coyote feels sorry for Eagle and wants to help him find food.

_____ 2. In "Coyote Steals the Sun and Moon," what is the reason Coyote gives for wanting light?
   A. He wants to learn to fly and needs light to see how Eagle does it.
   B. He says that he needs light to hunt.
   C. He believes that light will attract more insects for him to eat.
   D. He needs light to be able to see the sacred dancing.

_____ 3. Which of these supplies the light in the Zuñi myth about Coyote and Eagle?
   A. the sun
   B. fire
   C. fireflies
   D. all of the above

_____ 4. In "Coyote Steals the Sun and Moon," why does Eagle let Coyote carry the box?
   A. The box is heavy, and he wants to slow Coyote down.
   B. He realizes that he has hurt Coyote's feelings and wants to show that he trusts Coyote.
   C. He knows that if he does not give Coyote the box, Coyote will simply take it.
   D. He is tired of Coyote's pestering, and it is the custom to grant a request made four times.

_____ 5. Why does Coyote open the lid of the box in "Coyote Steals the Sun and the Moon"?
   A. He wants the light to rush up to the sky.
   B. He wants to annoy Eagle.
   C. He wants to show how brave he is.
   D. He is curious to see what is inside.

____ 6. Whom does Eagle blame for what happens at the end of the myth about Coyote and him?

    A. Coyote

    B. the gods

    C. the Kachinas

    D. himself

____ 7. Which event would you be most likely to include in a summary of "Coyote Steals the Sun and Moon"?

    A. Coyote and Eagle visit a pueblo.

    B. The people give Coyote and Eagle food.

    C. Coyote points to two boxes.

    D. The Kachinas do a dance that is sacred.

____ 8. Which event would you be *least* likely to include in a summary of "Coyote Steals the Sun and Moon"?

    A. Coyote hunts with Eagle.

    B. Coyote eats insects.

    C. Coyote and Eagle steal the box.

    D. The sun and moon fly away to the sky.

____ 9. Which word best describes Coyote in "Coyote Steals the Sun and Moon"?

    A. honest

    B. devious

    C. generous

    D. shy

____ 10. What is the main idea that "Coyote Steals the Sun and Moon" tries to explain?

    A. how animals behave

    B. why it is important to share tasks

    C. why we have summer and winter

    D. the difference between right and wrong

____ 11. From "Coyote Steals the Sun and Moon," what can you conclude about the Zuñi?

    A. They live in villages called pueblos.

    B. They sometimes do sacred dancing.

    C. According to their customs, if someone asks four times, you should grant that person's wish.

    D. all of the above

____ 12. Based only on "Coyote Steals the Sun and Moon," which of these animals do you conclude you can find in the part of the Southwest where the Zuñi live?
   A. rabbits
   B. iguanas
   C. polar bears
   D. sparrows

Vocabulary and Grammar

____ 13. Which pair contains antonyms, or words with opposite meanings?
   A. sacred–religious
   B. pestering–ignoring
   C. shriveled–wrapped
   D. pursuit–chase

____ 14. What kind of sentence is the following?

After a while the Kachinas went home to sleep, and Eagle scooped up the large box and flew off.

   A. simple
   B. compound
   C. complex
   D. compound-complex

____ 15. When you travel, carry as little as possible. Therefore, bring only what is

   _____.

   A. essential
   B. sacred
   C. organized
   D. disorganized

Essay

16. In a short essay, summarize "Coyote Steals the Sun and Moon." Tell what aspect of nature the myth explains, and give the important details of that explanation.

17. In a short essay, describe the personality of Coyote as you learn about it in "Coyote Steals the Sun and Moon." Identify the human qualities he displays, and tell how his behavior shows those qualities.

"Coyote Steals the Sun and Moon" retold by Richard Erdoes and Alfonso Ortiz
Selection Test B

Critical Reading *Identify the letter of the choice that best completes the statement or answers the question.*

_____ 1. In "Coyote Steals the Sun and Moon," how does Coyote get Eagle to hunt with him?
A. Coyote argues, "Two can catch more than one."
B. Coyote promises to give Eagle light if Eagle helps him hunt.
C. Coyote asks Eagle four times, after which Eagle is obliged to agree.
D. Coyote makes Eagle feel sorry for him by saying, "You have wings; I just have hair."

_____ 2. In "Coyote Steals the Sun and Moon," what does Eagle show about himself when he agrees to hunt with Coyote?
A. He is good natured and persuadable.
B. He is adventurous and brave.
C. He is clever and mischievous.
D. He is a talented hunter.

_____ 3. What do the details of "Coyote Steals the Sun and Moon" suggest about the landscape of the Southwest?
A. It is very dry, and there are no rivers.
B. It is rainy, and there are many rivers.
C. Coyotes, eagles, and rabbits live there.
D. all of the above

_____ 4. Which statement best summarizes Coyote and Eagle's visit to the pueblo in "Coyote Steals the Sun and Moon"?
A. Coyote and Eagle visit a pueblo and see some Kachinas.
B. Coyote and Eagle cross a wide river. They come to a pueblo and watch sacred dancing.
C. They visit a pueblo where Kachinas are dancing. They take a box with light in it.
D. They visit a pueblo, become Kachinas, do sacred dances, and take a box with light in it.

_____ 5. In "Coyote Steals the Sun and Moon," why does Eagle agree to steal the box of light?
A. He is a born thief.
B. He agrees that the Kachinas will probably not lend them the box.
C. He wants to keep the light all to himself.
D. all of the above

_____ 6. In "Coyote Steals the Sun and Moon," why does Coyote offer to carry the box of light?
A. He doesn't trust Eagle to do anything.
B. He is afraid that Eagle will not share it.
C. He wants to be more important.
D. He sees that it is slowing Eagle down.

___ 7. In "Coyote Steals the Sun and Moon," when Coyote tells Eagle, "You're the chief, and I'm just Coyote," what is he trying to do?
A. show his humility
B. escape his responsibilities
C. trick Eagle into doing Coyote's work
D. flatter Eagle into giving up the box

___ 8. Compared with Coyote in "Coyote Steals the Sun and Moon," what is Eagle like?
A. Eagle is more honest than Coyote.
B. Eagle is less clever than Coyote.
C. Eagle is a better hunter than Coyote.
D. all of the above

___ 9. Which statement best summarizes Coyote's behavior in "Coyote Steals the Sun and Moon"?
A. Although he is clever, he behaves foolishly in the end.
B. Although he is devious, he behaves nobly in the end.
C. Although he is talkative, he is silent in the end.
D. Although he is weak, he grows stronger in the end.

___ 10. What does the behavior of characters in "Coyote Steals the Sun and Moon" show about Zuñi customs or values?
A. Strangers were not welcome.
B. Borrowing was seen as stealing.
C. Sharing work was considered sensible.
D. Dancing was considered sinful.

___ 11. Based on "Coyote Steals the Sun and Moon," which of these conclusions can one draw about Zuñi culture?
A. Insects were an important part of their diet.
B. They got some of their food by hunting.
C. They were nomads who never settled down.
D. all of the above

___ 12. After Coyote loses the sun in "Coyote Steals the Sun and Moon," winter comes to cause great suffering. What does this detail tell you about the Zuñi way of life?
A. The Zuñi live in the desert and are not familiar with winter.
B. The Zuñi blame Coyote for what happened, and they think he is heartless and stupid.
C. The Zuñi rely on agriculture and need favorable weather.
D. The Zuñi worship the sun.

___ 13. What is the main purpose of "Coyote Steals the Sun and Moon"?
A. to help people understand how animals behave
B. to show young children the importance of sharing tasks
C. to explain the origin of winter
D. to teach the difference between right and wrong

Vocabulary and Grammar

___ 14. Which is most likely to be described as *shriveled*?
A. an umbrella
B. a clown
C. a jacket
D. a prune

___ 15. In which sentence is the underlined word used correctly?
A. To keep the sun's rays from harming you, sunscreen is <u>essential</u>.
B. The mother tried hard to <u>extract</u> the child's attention.
C. The wind blows the leaves into an <u>organized</u> pile.
D. In the operating room, doctors and nurses need to be very <u>disorganized</u>.

___ 16. What type of sentence is the following statement?
So it went for a stretch, and then Coyote started again.

A. simple
B. compound
C. complex
D. compound-complex

___ 17. Which choice combines these three sentences into one complex sentence?
Coyote opened the box. The moon flew into the sky. Then, the sun flew into the sky.

A. Coyote opened the box, and the moon and the sun flew into the sky.
B. When Coyote opened the box, the moon flew into the sky, and then the sun flew into the sky.
C. When Coyote opened the box, the moon and then the sun flew into the sky.
D. From the box opened by Coyote, the moon and then the sun flew into the sky.

Essay

18. In an essay, state a lesson about human behavior that "Coyote Steals the Sun and Moon" teaches. Then, show how the events and details in the myth point to this lesson.

19. In an essay, compare and contrast Coyote and Eagle as they are portrayed in "Coyote Steals the Sun and Moon." Consider their personalities, talents, attitudes, and behavior in particular situations. Also, discuss how one character influences the other.

Vocabulary Warm-up Word Lists

Study these words from the selections. Then, complete the activities.

Word List A

accord [uh KAWRD] *n.* doing something without being asked
   Brett surprised us by taking out the garbage of his own <u>accord</u>.

cyclone [SY klohn] *n.* tornado; a storm with strong winds
   The <u>cyclone</u> roared through town, damaging many houses.

poets [POH uhts] *n.* people who write poems
   Some <u>poets</u> write their poems in rhyme, while others don't.

recited [ri SYT id] *v.* said aloud from memory
   On July 4, an actor <u>recited</u> the Declaration of Independence.

shame [SHAYM] *n.* embarrassment or loss of honor
   Will blurted the answer without thinking and felt <u>shame</u> afterward.

spinning [SPIN ing] *n.* the telling of stories that you have made up
   While <u>spinning</u> tales of the Wild West, the storyteller showed slides.

straddling [STRAD ling] *adj.* with legs on either side of something
   Betty rode the donkey with her legs loosely <u>straddling</u> the animal.

yarns [yahrnz] *n.* long tales that are not completely true
   Late nights around the campfire, we told <u>yarns</u> of pirates and sailors.

Word List B

boasted [BOHST id] *v.* bragged
   Hilary <u>boasted</u> that she could run a mile in five minutes.

compete [kuhm PEET] *v.* to try to win or be better
   We must <u>compete</u> against South High for the city title.

furthermore [FER <u>th</u>er mawr] *adv.* in addition
   You must finish dusting; <u>furthermore</u>, you have to wash the floor.

instructed [in STRUHKT id] *v.* told someone what to do
   The hotel guest <u>instructed</u> the desk clerk to wake her at eight.

predicted [pri DIKT id] *v.* said what you think will happen
   Weather forecasters <u>predicted</u> a foot of snow for the weekend.

riverbed [RIV er bed] *n.* the ground over which a river flows
   Without rain for months, there was nothing left but a dry <u>riverbed</u>.

weaving [WEEV ing] *n.* smooth combination of ideas and subjects
   The writer is an expert at <u>weaving</u> together facts and fiction.

whizzing [WIZ ing] *v.* speeding or moving quickly
   We didn't expect to see the train <u>whizzing</u> past our station.

"Chicoria" adapted by José Griego y Maestas, retold by Rudolfo A. Anaya
from **"The People, Yes"** by Carl Sandburg
Vocabulary Warm-up Exercises

Exercise A *Fill in each blank in the paragraph below with an appropriate word from Word List A. Use each word only once.*

In our little town, there were no published [1] _____ or novelists. Yet, just about everyone loved to stay up nights telling and listening to [2] _____ of pioneer days. Sometimes, friends took turns and [3] _____ parts of a well-known tale. Other times, they made up new ones. No one had to be coaxed to speak, but did it of his or her own [4] _____. In [5] _____ tales of olden times, our townsfolk could cause any professional storyteller great [6] _____. My favorite tale was of the [7] _____ of '79. That twister was so mighty, it was supposedly lifted our first mayor and his horse hundreds of feet into the air. When they came down, there was the trusty horse, [8] _____ the mayor!

Exercise B *Revise each sentence so that the underlined vocabulary words are used in a logical way. Be sure to keep the vocabulary words in your revision.*

1. We saw cars <u>whizzing</u> along on the highway at 25 miles an hour.
   _____

2. We <u>boasted</u> that we could not <u>compete</u> with any other soccer team.
   _____

3. We <u>predicted</u> that we were late, and <u>furthermore</u>, that we were on time.
   _____

4. During the flood, we could walk right in the <u>riverbed</u>.
   _____

5. The master <u>instructed</u> his servants not to do anything he told them.
   _____

6. In <u>weaving</u> a twisty tale of suspense, the movie director used lots of comic effects.
   _____

"Chicoria" adapted by José Griego y Maestas, retold by Rudolfo A. Anaya
from **"The People, Yes"** by Carl Sandburg
Reading Warm-up A

Read the following passage. Pay special attention to the underlined words. Then, read it again, and complete the activities. Use a separate sheet of paper for your written answers.

Where do those <u>yarns</u> we call tall tales come from? Why are they still popular today?

Gathering to hear stories and poems is a very old form of entertainment. Before radio, television, and movies, people amused one another by <u>spinning</u> stories. <u>Poets</u> spoke their verses for others to hear and pass on.

Settlers on the frontier were the first to tell tall tales. These stories, full of daring deeds and folksy humor, captured people's imaginations. Some tales told about fictional heroes. Others revealed larger-than-life stories about real people, such as Davy Crockett, Daniel Boone, and Johnny Appleseed.

Pecos Bill, another heroic character, was a cowboy. He made friends with wild animals and even rode a mountain lion instead of a horse. He was seen <u>straddling</u> a <u>cyclone</u> to bring that twister under control.

John Henry was the hero of railroad workers. He could hammer spikes into railroad tracks faster than anyone else. When a machine is invented to do the job, John Henry decides—of his own <u>accord</u>—to try to beat the machine. He does, but dies wearing himself out. Of course, there is no <u>shame</u> in that!

Daniel Boone and Davy Crockett, real-life characters, lived colorful lives on the frontier. Stories about them made their lives more amazing. Crockett himself <u>recited</u> many of the stories about his feats.

Johnny Appleseed was the nickname of John Chapman. In real life, he traveled the wilderness planting apple trees. Many stories grew up around this gentle man who believed that beautiful fruit orchards would improve settlers' lives.

We still enjoy tall tales today because they are so entertaining. In a way, comic-book superheroes of today are like tall-tale heroes. Both are larger-than-life characters give people hope in a difficult world.

1. Circle two words that tell what <u>yarns</u> are. Name one of your favorite *yarns*.

2. Circle the word in paragraph three that means about the same as <u>spinning</u>? Explain what *spinning* means.

3. Underline what <u>poets</u> spoke aloud. Name one of your favorite *poets*.

4. Circle the word in the previous sentence that gives a clue to the meaning of <u>straddling</u>. Describe what *straddling* a *cyclone* might look like.

5. Underline the word that gives a clue to the meaning of <u>accord</u>. Describe something that you did of your own *accord*.

6. Underline the words in the previous sentence that tell what there is no <u>shame</u> in. Rewrite the sentence with *shame,* substituting a word or phrase with the same meaning.

7. Circle the words that tell what Crocket <u>recited</u>. Name something that you have *recited* lately.

Name _____ Date _____

"Chicoria" adapted by José Griego y Maestas, retold by Rudolfo A. Anaya
from **"The People, Yes"** by Carl Sandburg
Reading Warm-up B

Read the following passage. Pay special attention to the underlined words. Then, read it again, and complete the activities. Use a separate sheet of paper for your written answers.

"I will become the best writer in all of New Mexico," boasted Angel Mejias. "They will call me Angelito and come from far and wide to listen to me reading my works."

"I have instructed my ears not to listen to such bragging anymore," replied Margarita. "And my ears always listen to what I command them; furthermore, I will tell your mouth not to spout such nonsense, either. Here, I'm doing it right now!"

The occasion for this conversation was breakfast the week before Angel was going to compete in his school poetry contest. As he had written exactly two lines of poetry up to that day, his sister was understandably doubtful.

"You know that everyone predicted great things for me when I was born," Angel said after a long pause. "That's because the night I entered this life there was a ring around the moon."

"The only thing I've noticed that is great about you is your appetite," Margarita replied.

"Very funny," said Angel, but secretly, he feared she was right. Writing poetry seemed like trying to send stones whizzing across the surface of a stream when there was only a dry riverbed.

That night, Angel had a dream. He was standing in the center of a circle of people, describing how he had become a writer. He stood there confidently, weaving jokes, funny stories, and other personal bits into his talk. There was great applause.

The next day, Angel announced to Margarita that he was not entering the poetry contest after all. While he told her about his dream, she shook her head and rolled her eyes.

"I'm not surprised," she said. "I always knew you were not a poet but a joker."

1. Circle the word in the next paragraph that hints at the meaning of <u>boasted</u>. Write about a time you *boasted*.

2. Underline a word in the next sentence that means nearly the same as <u>instructed</u>. Tell about something someone *instructed* you to do.

3. Circle the two smaller words in <u>furthermore</u>. Write two sentences. Begin the second with *furthermore*.

4. Underline the word that gives a clue to the meaning of <u>compete</u>. Describe something that you like to *compete* in.

5. Circle the words that tell what was <u>predicted</u> What have you *predicted*?

6. Circle the word that tells what is <u>whizzing</u>. Tell about something you have seen *whizzing* by.

7. Circle the word describing the <u>riverbed</u>. Tell whether water can flow on this *riverbed*.

8. Underline the word that tells who was doing the <u>weaving</u>. How would you go about *weaving* jokes into a talk?

53

Name _____   Date _____

"Chicoria" adapted by José Griego y Maestas, retold by Rudolfo A. Anaya
from **"The People, Yes"** by Carl Sandburg
Reading: Use a Graphic to Summarize Literature

A **summary** is a short statement that presents the main points of a piece of writing. Since a summary leaves out the less important details, it provides a quick way to preview or review a much longer work and focus on what is most important in it. You also will use a summary of a work as part of your discussion of the work.

In the passage from "The People, Yes," Carl Sandburg presents summaries of more than twenty American folk tales, which he calls "yarns." Each summary can complete his opening statement, "They have yarns. . . ." For example, lines 1–7 can read as "They have yarns of a skyscraper. . . . They have yarns of one corn crop. . . . They have yarns of pancakes so thin. . . ."

DIRECTIONS: *Write a summary of "Chicoria" that could have appeared as an item in "The People, Yes." Before you write the summary, determine which events or ideas from "Chicoria" are important enough to include. Use a graphic aid such as a cluster diagram or a time line to organize the important events or ideas.*

Graphic Aid

Summary

They have yarns _____

_____

_____

_____

_____

_____

54

"Chicoria" adapted by José Griego y Maestas, retold by Rudolfo A. Anaya
from **"The People, Yes"** by Carl Sandburg
Literary Analysis: Oral Tradition

Although "The People, Yes" is a piece of written literature, it pulls together many stories from the American **oral tradition,** which is the body of stories, poems, and songs passed down by word of mouth from one generation to the next. The yarns and legends of oral tradition often contain exaggeration, references to magic, and other invented details that do not reflect reality. At the same time, they often have some basis in actual fact. Consider, for example, Sandburg's summary of a yarn about a corn crop:

They have yarns . . .

Of one corn crop in Missouri when the roots

Went so deep and drew off so much water

The Mississippi riverbed that year was dry. . . .

Although no corn crop could cause the Mississippi riverbed to go dry, it is a fact that corn was grown in Missouri along the Mississippi River, and the yarn probably had its origins in a time when a Mississippi drought followed a good corn crop.

DIRECTIONS: *Identify another yarn that Sandburg summarizes in "The People, Yes."*
Then, from the summary, list one exaggerated detail and one factual detail.

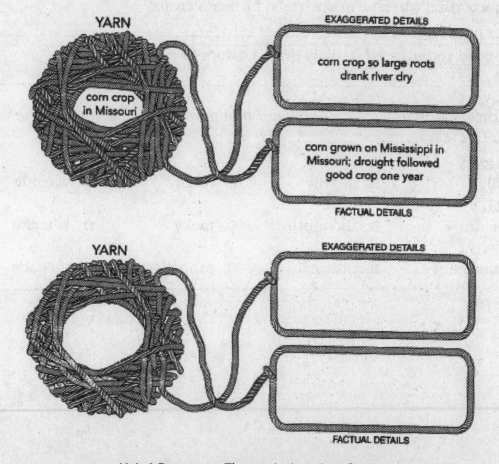

YARN

com crop in Missouri

EXAGGERATED DETAILS

corn crop so large roots drank river dry

corn grown on Mississippi in Missouri; drought followed good crop one year

FACTUAL DETAILS

YARN

EXAGGERATED DETAILS

FACTUAL DETAILS

Name _____ Date _____

"Chicoria" adapted by José Griego y Maestas, retold by Rudolfo A. Anaya
from "The People, Yes" by Carl Sandburg
Vocabulary Builder

A. DIRECTIONS: *Write* T *if the statement is true or* F *if the statement is false.*

____ 1. A *cyclone* can cause terrible destruction and loss of life.

____ 2. Most people enjoy the company of a *haughty* person.

____ 3. Waiters and waitresses who treat customers *cordially* rarely get tipped.

B. DIRECTIONS: *Answer the questions with complete sentences, using each Word List word only once.*

Word List

cordially	haughty	cyclone

1. In some fairy tales, does the queen act proud and superior?

   _____

2. Could a rotating windstorm destroy a farmer's crops?

   _____

3. Does a good receptionist usually greet visitors in a friendly way?

   _____

C. DIRECTIONS: *Circle the letter of the word that is closest in meaning to the word in* CAPITAL LETTERS.

1. CORDIALLY :
   A. coldly   B. angrily   C. dizzily   D. warmly
2. HAUGHTY :
   A. scornful   B. thoughtful   C. tacky   D. whacky
3. CYCLONE :
   A. amusement   B. blizzard   C. propeller   D. tornado

Name _____ Date _____

"Chicoria" adapted by José Griego y Maestas, retold by Rudolfo A. Anaya
from **"The People, Yes"** by Carl Sandburg
Support for Writing a Critical Analysis

Use this chart to gather examples of dialect, folk idioms, hyperbole, and other elements of the oral tradition that you plan to discuss in your critical analysis. For the location of an example from "The People, Yes," use *TPY* and a line number; for an example from "Chicoria," use *Chic* and a paragraph number. An example has been done for you.

Type	Example	Location	Effect on Tone or Mood
Dialect	Californio	Chic 4	makes selection seem more authentic; stresses the contempt New Mexicans have for California poets
Idiom (expression that has a meaning particular to a language or region)			
Hyperbole (exaggeration)			
Other element of oral tradition			

Now, explain how the examples you collected affect the tone and the mood of folk literature.

"Chicoria" adapted by José Griego y Maestas, retold by Rudolfo A. Anaya
from **"The People, Yes"** by Carl Sandburg
Support for Extend Your Learning

Research and Technology

Use the chart below to record information about the folk tales or stories you choose.

Title and Source	Why I Chose It	Historical/Cultural Background

Listening and Speaking

Complete this tip sheet with specific advice for the four topics.

Tip Sheet For Storytellers			
How to Find a Story to Tell	What Kind of Eye Contact to Make	How to Use Voice and Body	How to Add Humor to Storytelling

Name _____ Date _____

"Chicoria" adapted by José Griego y Maestas, retold by Rudolfo A. Anaya
from **"The People, Yes"** by Carl Sandburg
Enrichment: How Jobs Change

In summarizing tales for "The People, Yes," Carl Sandburg touches on many jobs that Americans have held. Some of those jobs still exist; others no longer do because society has changed or technology has erased a need.

A. DIRECTIONS: *List some of the jobs specifically stated or implied in the selection. For each, indicate the line of the poem that mentions the job, and give a brief general description of the job. The first has been done for you as an example.*

	Job	Line/s	General Job Description
1.	architect	1	designs buildings
2.			
3.			
4.			
5.			
6.			

B. DIRECTIONS: *From the jobs you listed, choose one that has been affected by technological changes. Then, answer the following questions about the job. Use your own knowledge and experience, or conduct library or online research to help you answer the second question.*

Job affected by technology: _____

1. What does the poem state or imply about the nature of this job?

_____

_____

2. How has this job changed since the poem was published in 1936? How has it remained the same?

_____

_____

_____

_____

_____

_____

Name _____ Date _____

"Chicoria" adapted by José Griego y Maestas, retold by Rudolfo A. Anaya
from **"The People, Yes"** by Carl Sandburg
Selection Test A

Critical Reading *Identify the letter of the choice that best answers the question.*

____ 1. In "Chicoria," what does the man named Chicoria come to California to do?
    A. attend a dinner
    B. win a bet with the rancher's servant
    C. compete with a poet named Gracia
    D. help with the seasonal ranch work

____ 2. In "Chicoria," what bet does Chicoria make with one of the rancher's servants?
    A. He bets that he will win the poetry contest.
    B. He bets that he will sit down and eat with the rancher and his guest.
    C. He bets that he can take the place of the serving girl and not be detected.
    D. all of the above

____ 3. Which phrase best describes the character Chicoria?
    A. clever and confident
    B. foolish and boastful
    C. shy and retiring
    D. powerful and brave

____ 4. From his behavior, what can you conclude about the rancher in "Chicoria"?
    A. He does not have enough food to feed his guests.
    B. He is not used to treating poorer people with respect.
    C. He believes all people deserve the same amount of respect.
    D. He is not only rude but also cruel.

____ 5. If you were writing a summary of "Chicoria," which statement would you most likely include?
    A. New Mexican poets include Vilmas, Cinfuego, Cebolleta, and the Black Poet.
    B. Chicoria bets that the master will invite him to the dinner table.
    C. A serving maid watches the dinner events.
    D. Chicoria says that New Mexican goats are different from Californian goats.

____ 6. Which word is an example of Mexican American dialect in "Chicoria"?
    A. Chicoria
    B. Gracia
    C. Californio
    D. cyclone

_____ 7. Which characteristic of oral literature is true of "Chicoria"?

A. It explains a mystery of nature.

B. The hero is larger than life.

C. The language is formal.

D. It reveals aspects of the culture that produced it.

_____ 8. To which culture does the passage from "The People, Yes" most often refer?

A. Mexican

B. British

C. French

D. American

_____ 9. According to "The People, Yes," how was the boy who climbed the cornstalk kept from starving?

A. He stopped to eat ears of corn on the way up.

B. People tossed biscuits to him.

C. He had brought a supply of food with him.

D. He found plenty to eat when he reached the top.

_____ 10. "The People, Yes" mentions skyscrapers that needed hinges on the two top stories to let the moon go by. What does this image exaggerate about the skyscrapers?

A. their use as business offices

B. their modern appearance

C. their light coloring

D. their height

_____ 11. In "The People, Yes," what characteristic is shared by the yarn about Pecos Pete riding the cyclone and the yarn about the man driving a swarm of bees?

A. Both exaggerate size.

B. Both exaggerate speed.

C. Both exaggerate a person's ability or accomplishment.

D. Both avoid the exaggeration of the other yarns.

_____ 12. "The People, Yes" refers to a yarn about "pancakes so thin they had only one side." What does this image tell you about the people who originated the yarn?

A. They introduced pancakes to Americans.

B. They knew little about the laws of science—a pancake must have two sides.

C. They had little imagination and were not very creative in their storytelling.

D. They had a sharp sense of humor and enjoyed making up exaggerated stories.

Vocabulary and Grammar

____ 13. Which word is an antonym for *cordially*?
  A. seriously
  B. warmly
  C. wisely
  D. rudely

____ 14. To do well on a test, most people find it _____ to study.
  A. essential
  B. organized
  C. disorganized
  D. haughty

____ 15. Where should commas be added in this sentence?
  Carl Sandburg tells about Pecos Pete Paul Bunyan and John Henry.
  A. after *Pete* only
  B. after *Pete* and *Bunyan*
  C. after *Bunyan* only
  D. nowhere; the sentence is correct as is

Essay

16. In a short essay, summarize the folk tale "Chicoria." Tell what happens to the characters during the episode and what you think they teach or learn.

17. In a short essay, demonstrate that the yarns in the selection from "The People, Yes" use exaggeration. Give two examples of summarized yarns, and explain what each one exaggerates.

"Chicoria" adapted by José Griego y Maestas, retold by Rudolfo A. Anaya
from **"The People, Yes"** by Carl Sandburg
Selection Test B

Critical Reading *Identify the letter of the choice that best completes the statement or answers the question.*

_____ 1. In "Chicoria," what bet does Chicoria make with one of the rancher's servants?
   A. He bets that he will beat Gracia in a poetry contest.
   B. He bets that he will get invited to dine at the rancher's table.
   C. Both *a* and *b* are correct.
   D. Neither *a* nor *b* is correct.

_____ 2. In "Chicoria," how is the character Chicoria different from the rancher's servants?
   A. He is more self-confident.
   B. He is a harder worker.
   C. He is fatter.
   D. He is not as clever.

_____ 3. Which statement best summarizes "Chicoria"?
   A. A rich rancher shows bad manners by not inviting a poor guest to dine with him.
   B. A poet comes to a ranch in New Mexico to participate in a poetry contest.
   C. A servant tells a visitor what to expect from the master and makes a bet with him about it.
   D. A poor but clever poet gets himself invited to eat with a rich rancher, thus winning a bet.

_____ 4. From the details in "Chicoria," which of these was valued by the southwestern culture that produced the tale?
   A. poetry
   B. heritage
   C. good manners
   D. all of the above

_____ 5. From the details in "Chicoria," what can you conclude about California in Chicoria's day?
   A. It was strictly divided into social classes.
   B. It was a society in which people were treated equally regardless of wealth or background.
   C. The most influential and wealthy people were poets and philosophers.
   D. Poor people knew little about their culture.

_____ 6. What role does dialect play in "Chicoria"?
   A. It retains the oral quality of the old tale.
   B. It makes the characters' speech realistic.
   C. It adds authentic local flavor to the tale.
   D. all of the above

____ 7. Which statement best summarizes the selection from "The People, Yes"?
A. The selection offers summaries of tall tales from all over America.
B. The selection provides details about farm life in the Midwest.
C. The selection shows the unusual effects of cyclones.
D. The selection gives realistic accounts of everyday American life.

____ 8. What does the selection from "The People, Yes" show about Americans?
A. They have a big and diverse oral tradition.
B. They are unrealistic people.
C. They prefer serious literature to humor.
D. all of the above

____ 9. What do almost all the yarns in the passage from "The People, Yes" have in common?
A. They deal with unusual farm animals.
B. They celebrate heroes such as Paul Bunyan.
C. They use a child's point of view.
D. They tell of the scientifically impossible.

____ 10. "The People, Yes" mentions a yarn about an old man whose whiskers arrived a day before he did. What does this description suggest?
A. The old man's whiskers were very long.
B. The wind was very strong.
C. The old man was not very clever.
D. The old man was on a slow stagecoach.

____ 11. In "The People, Yes," what is the purpose of the yarn about "pigs so thin the farmer had to tie knots in their tails to keep them from crawling through the cracks in their pens"?
A. to wittily tell why pigs' tails are curled
B. to distinguish a pig from a hog
C. to remind farmers to build strong pig pens
D. to depict farmers' everyday struggles

____ 12. From the details in the yarns in "The People, Yes," what can you conclude about American life when the yarns arose?
A. Farming was more widespread then.
B. Cyclones were more common then.
C. Skyscrapers were more common then.
D. all of the above

Vocabulary and Grammar

____ 13. Which of these people is most likely to be described as *haughty*?
A. a humble tailor
B. a demanding opera singer
C. a friendly hotel receptionist
D. a funny clown

____ 14. Where would you be most likely to find the word *cordially*?
   A. in an ad for a clothing sale
   B. in a weather forecast
   C. in the closing of a letter
   D. in a bank ledger recording payments

____ 15. In which sentence is the underlined word used correctly?
   A. For a healthy diet, protein is <u>essential</u>.
   B. The movie star sparkled in <u>sequence</u>.
   C. The cutting machine <u>organized</u> the cow.
   D. <u>Extract</u> this essay with more evidence.

____ 16. Where should commas be added in this sentence?
   Drawing on folklore Carl Sandburg mentions several yarns stories in the oral tradition.
   A. after *folklore* only
   B. after *folklore* and *Sandburg*
   C. after *folklore* and *yarns*
   D. after *yarns* only

____ 17. Which sentence needs one or more commas added?
   A. Because the wind was so cold, the captain's shadow froze to the deck of the ship.
   B. The corn roots sucked up the water, and the riverbed went dry.
   C. Chicoria a poet from New Mexico was invited to California.
   D. The brown eggs were square instead of round.

Essay

18. In an essay, explain what "Chicoria" shows about the importance of poetry and story-telling. Discuss the character Chicoria, the talents he shows, and the way those talents affect his own life and the lives of other characters.

19. The selection from "The People, Yes" tells about oral literature from the 1800s and the early 1900s. Write an essay in which you discuss some of the things that oral literature shows about American life in those days. Among other things, you might consider people's jobs, pastimes, and other activities; the forms of transportation they used; the kinds of stories they told; and their relationship with nature.

Vocabulary Warm-up Word Lists

Study these words from "Brer Possum's Dilemma." They are all dialect words from the Old South, where this tale originated. Regional dialect is the language of everyday speech in an area. Some writers use dialect to capture the speech of their characters. If you find this language hard to understand, try reading the words aloud. Then, complete the activities.

Word List A

a-doin' [uh-DOO-in] *v.* doing
   He was always busy <u>a-doin'</u> something for others.

Brer [BRER] *n.* brother; used before a name
   <u>Brer</u> Rabbit walked down the road and met <u>Brer</u> Fox.

critters [KRIT erz] *n.* creatures; animals
   He didn't like to see <u>critters</u>, large or small; in trouble.

offa [AWF uh] *prep.* off of
   Won't you help get that tree limb <u>offa</u> me?

outa [OWT uh] *prep.* out of
   I need a ladder to get the cat <u>outa</u> the tree.

you's [YOOZ] *contraction* you is; standard English, you are
   <u>You's</u> too kindhearted to say a bad word to anyone.

Word List B

agin [uh-GIN] *adv.* again
   Let's go over the directions <u>agin</u>.

'cause [KAWZ] *conj.* because; for the reason that
   I should go home now <u>'cause</u> company is arriving soon.

feller [FEL er] *n.* fellow; guy
   Now, some folks think Brer Rabbit is a fine <u>feller</u>.

'im [im] *pron.* him
   If my dad is asleep on the porch, don't bother <u>'im</u>.

ol' [ohl] *adj.* old
   If you get that mean <u>ol'</u> rattlesnake riled up, there will be trouble.

reckon [REK uhn] *v.* to think or assume
   I <u>reckon</u> I've been asleep for six hours.

"Brer Possum's Dilemma" by Jackie Torrence
"John Henry" Traditional
Vocabulary Warm-up Exercises

Exercise A *Fill in each blank in the paragraph below with an appropriate dialect word from Word List A. Use each word only once.*

[1] _____ in for a real treat when you read about

[2] _____ Rabbit and his friends. Of all the [3] _____

of the fields and woods, he was the trickiest. He was always [4] _____

something to get himself into the worst trouble. Then, he had to be clever to get himself

[5] _____ the trouble. There was one time when he got stuck on a tar

baby. The fox had made this figure out of tar to catch the troublesome rabbit. The rab-

bit, however, was so clever that he got the fox to pull him [6] _____ the

tar baby. How did he do that? Read the tale to find out.

Exercise B *Write a complete sentence to answer each question. For each answer, use a dialect word from Word List B to replace each underlined word or group of words without changing its meaning.*

1. What's the name of a <u>guy</u> who's a hero in your life?

_____

2. Do you <u>assume</u> your summer vacation will be busy?

_____

3. Can you tell me <u>one more time</u> what the radius of a circle is?

_____

4. Are you careful when you cross streets <u>for the reason that</u> there's heavy traffic?

_____

5. Do you think you'll mind growing <u>aged</u>?

_____

6. If you had a male dog, what would you call <u>him</u>?

_____

Name _____ Date _____

"**Brer Possum's Dilemma**" by Jackie Torrence
"**John Henry**" Traditional
Reading Warm-up A

Read the following passage. Pay special attention to the underlined words. Then, read it again, and complete the activities. Use a separate sheet of paper for your written answers.

Brer, or "Brother" Rabbit and the other beloved critters of the Old South did not spring from the mind of writer Joel Chandler Harris, as some people used to think. Harris is the author known for introducing whites in America to African American tales that use dialect, or local speech.

Harris was a teenager in Georgia. After the Civil War, he remembered stories that slaves had told him and recorded them. He then invented a character he called Uncle Remus to be the storyteller. Many versions of the stories, including ones about Brer Rabbit, exist today.

Actually, the character of Brer Rabbit had its origins before the pre-Civil War South. There was a long tradition of trickster tales in African folk tales. African storytellers later brought their tales to America. In the new land, they created tales in which animals took on the traits of people among whom they lived.

The stories of Brer Rabbit and his world are all the livelier for the southern dialect that is used in them. Here are some examples. Brer Fox would not say, "I see what you are doing." Instead, he would say, "I see what you's a-doin'. Brer Rabbit wouldn't think, "I can get myself out of this trouble." Instead, he would think, "I kin git myself outa dis trouble." Nor would he announce, "I just have to get off of this log and run as fast as I can." Instead, he would think, "I jist gotta git offa dis log and run lickety split."

The rhythm of this speech is natural and musical. Just listen as the storytellers of long ago spin their delicious tales. It's no wonder these tales have lasted and become favorites today.

1. Circle the word that is standard English for brer. Write a sentence in which you use *Brer* with another animal name.

2. Write the standard English word for critters. List some of the *critters* that appeared in African American folk tales.

3. Circle the words in standard English that mean the same as you's. Following that example, write this sentence in dialect: *We are going now.*

4. Write the standard English for a-doin'. Following the example of *a-doin'*, write a sentence using the dialect form of *hoping.*

5. Circle the words in standard English that mean the same as outa and offa. Following these examples, write the words *full of* in dialect and then use the new word in a sentence.

Name _____ Date _____

"Brer Possum's Dilemma" by Jackie Torrence
"John Henry" Traditional
Reading Warm-up B

Read the following passage. Pay special attention to the underlined words. Then, read it again, and complete the activities. Use a separate sheet of paper for your written answers.

African American folk tales about Brer Rabbit and the other talking animals of the woods and fields date from the pre-Civil War South. They are fun to read or listen to, and they also offer observations on life. Often, the stories are still told today in the dialect, or regional speech, such as this example.

Ol' Brer Fox tries to trick Ol' Brer Rabbit, but Brer Rabbit always gets away. Just when it looks like Brer Rabbit might be a goner, he tricks Brex Fox into saving 'im. Once agin, he gets the better of Brer Fox.

Talking animal stories go back to ancient times. Some of the ones we know best today are in the collection of short tales known as Aesop's Fables. Each of the tales ends with a moral, or message, that expresses some idea about life.

For example, there is the story of the tortoise or turtle, and the hare. The hare challenges the tortoise to a race. He is so far ahead and so sure of winning that he takes a nap. In the meantime, the tortoise wins the race. The moral of the story is "Slow and steady wins the race."

The messages of the stories about Brer Rabbit and his friends are not always as clear as the ones in Aesop. If pressed to come up with a message of trickster tale, you might say something like this: "Do you reckon you are clever and tricky? Be sure you knows what you are doing 'cause when the other feller is clever and tricky too, you have to be more clever still and trickier."

1. Circle the two places where the writer uses Ol'. Write the word in standard English. Then, explain why you think the writer uses this word.

2. Circle the word that 'im refers to. Imagine *Brer* Rabbit were Sister Rabbit. Rewrite the sentence with 'im in it, replacing words to show that the rabbit is a female.

3. Circle the words that *once agin* refers back to. Rewrite the sentence with *agin* in standard English.

4. Circle the word in the next-to-last sentence that is in dialect. Write a sentence using that word in dialect.

5. Circle the two words in dialect in the last sentence. Then, explain whether you agree with the statement. Use the two circled words in standard English in your answer.

"Brer Possum's Dilemma" by Jackie Torrence
"John Henry" Traditional

Reading: Use a Graphic to Summarize Literature

A **summary** is a short statement that presents the main points of a piece of writing. Since a summary leaves out the less important details, it provides a quick way to preview or review a much longer work and focus on what is most important in it. You will also use a summary of a work as part of your discussion of the work.

Before you write a summary of a work of literature, determine whether an event or idea is important enough to include in your summary. Then, use a graphic aid such as a cluster diagram or a time line to organize the important events or ideas. For example, for a summary of the selection from "John Henry," you might use a time line like this one:

JH as baby	predicts death at Big Bend Tunnel
JH as worker	steam drill brought in
	JH claims he'll beat steam drill or die.
	JH points out captain's drill broke.
	JH hurts himself.
	JH dies from injuries.

DIRECTIONS: *Write a summary of "Brer Possum's Dilemma." Before you write, determine which events or ideas are important enough to include in the summary. Use a graphic aid such as a cluster diagram or a time line to organize the important events or ideas.*

Graphic Aid

Summary

_____

_____

_____

_____

_____

_____

_____

"Brer Possum's Dilemma" by Jackie Torrence
"John Henry" Traditional

Literary Analysis: Oral Tradition

Both "Brer Possum's Dilemma" and "John Henry" come from the American **oral tradition,** which is the body of stories, poems, and songs passed down by word of mouth from one generation to the next. Even when they are written down, the tales, poems, and songs from the oral tradition often use dialect to make them seem like spoken English. **Dialect** is the vocabulary and grammar spoken in a particular region or by a particular group. Because it differs from **standard English,** the most widely known and accepted form of the language, it may contain terms that puzzle you at first. To understand a puzzling dialect term, follow these steps:

- Consider whether it might mean the same as a more familiar word or phrase that it sounds like.
- Use its position in the sentence to help you determine its likely part of speech.
- Look for other clues about the term in its **context,** or surrounding words.
- Once you guess the meaning, replace the term with your guess to see if it makes sense.

A. DIRECTIONS: *Use the sound, position, and other context clues to figure out the meaning of each underlined dialect term. Then, circle the letter of the correct meaning.*

1. Back in the days when the animals could talk, there lived ol' Brer Possum. He was a fine <u>feller</u>.
   A. filler   B. fellow   C. dropper   D. cutter

2. Why, he never liked to see no <u>critters</u> in trouble. He was always helpin' out, a-doin' somethin' for others.
   A. quitters   B. critics   C. creatures   D. makers

3. <u>Cap'n</u> says to John Henry, "Gonna bring me a steam drill 'round."
   A. Captain   B. cap in   C. cape   D. Corporal

4. The rock so tall an' John Henry so small, / That he <u>lied</u> down his hammer an' he cried.
   A. told a falsehood   C. went to sleep
   B. sang   D. laid

B. DIRECTIONS: *Write your reaction to the use of dialect in the two selections. Do you find that dialect makes each selection more or less effective? Why?*

_____

_____

_____

_____

_____

"Brer Possum's Dilemma" by Jackie Torrence
"John Henry" Traditional
Vocabulary Builder

A. DIRECTIONS: *Write* T *if the statement is true or* F *if the statement is false.*

____ 1. A weeping child can be a *pitiful* sight.

____ 2. The month of December *commenced* on December 31.

B. DIRECTIONS: *Answer the questions with complete sentences, using each Word List word only once.*

Word List

commenced	pitiful

1. Is a motherless kitten a sight that arouses sympathy?

   _____

2. Has the twenty-first century started yet?

   _____

C. DIRECTIONS: *Circle the letter of the word that is closest in meaning to the word in* CAPITAL LETTERS.

1. COMMENCED:
   A. spoke
   B. observed
   C. ended
   D. began

2. PITIFUL:
   A. sad
   B. thoughtful
   C. angry
   D. emotional

"Brer Possum's Dilemma" by Jackie Torrence
"John Henry" Traditional
Support for Writing a Critical Analysis

Use this chart to gather examples of dialect, folk idioms, hyperbole, and other elements of the oral tradition that you plan to discuss in your critical analysis. For the location of an example from "Brer Possum's Dilemma," use *BPD* and a line number; for an example from "John Henry," use *JH* and a line number. An example has been done for you.

Type	Example	Location	Effect on Tone or Mood
Dialect	ol' Brer Possum	BPD 4	creates a folksy, familiar quality that makes the character more appealing
Idiom (expression that has a meaning particular to a language or region)			
Hyperbole (exaggeration)			
Other element of oral tradition			

Now, explain how the examples you collected affect the tone and the mood of folk literature.

Name _____ Date _____

Support for Extend Your Learning

Research and Technology

Use the chart below to record information about the folk tales or stories you choose.

Title and Source	Why I Chose It	Historical/Cultural Background

Listening and Speaking

Complete this tip sheet with specific advice for the four topics.

Tip Sheet For Storytellers			
How to Find a Story to Tell	What Kind of Eye Contact to Make	How to Use Voice and Body	How to Add Humor to Storytelling

"Brer Possum's Dilemma" by Jackie Torrence
"John Henry" Traditional

Enrichment: John Henry and Technological Change

In the 1800s, the development of railroads revolutionized transportation, but the job of laying railroad tracks all across America was difficult. Railroad companies hired thousands of men to smooth the terrain and cut through obstacles that stood in the way. Steel drivers like John Henry used long-handled hammers and spikes to pound holes into rocks. The holes were then be filled with explosives that would blast an opening in the mountain. The steel driver moved deeper and deeper until eventually the opening was deep enough for a railroad to pass through the mountain. Hoping to cut time and the expense of men, some tunnel engineers introduced steam drills. The conflict in "John Henry" arises when Henry's "Cap'n," or boss, considers such a drill.

The legend of John Henry is believed to be based on the exploits of an actual steel driver. While researchers debate whether he was born in North Carolina, Virginia, Alabama, or elsewhere, most agree that he was probably born as an African American slave in the 1840s or 1850s and that he grew to be an unusually large man for his day— at least six feet tall and two hundred pounds. Most versions of the legend tell about the famous contest while he worked on the Big Bend Tunnel, an actual railroad tunnel that was cut though more than a mile of mountain in Summers County, West Virginia, in the 1870s. The tunnel was part of the C. & O. Railroad, running from Chesapeake Bay in Virginia to the Ohio River Valley.

DIRECTIONS: *Answer these questions based on the song "John Henry," your own knowledge, and the information on this page.*

1. **A.** Given the dates, why is it likely that John Henry was born a slave?

   _____

   B. Does knowing that he was born a slave add significance to the song for you? Explain.

   _____

2. What do you think the *C* and *O* stood for in the name *C. & O. Railroad*?

   _____

3. **A.** How do you think steel drivers felt when steam drills were introduced? Why?

   _____

   B. How are these feelings reflected in the song?

   _____

4. Why do you think the real John Henry came to be portrayed as a hero?

   _____

   _____

   _____

"Chicoria" adapted by José Griego y Maestas, retold by Rudolfo A. Anaya
from **"The People, Yes"** by Carl Sandburg
"Brer Possum's Dilemma" by Jackie Torrence
"John Henry" Traditional

Build Language Skills: Vocabulary

The prefix *un-*

The prefix *un-* means "not." It is generally used to form antonyms, words that mean the opposite of other words. For example, *usual* means "common." When you add the prefix *un-*, you get *unusual*, which means "not usual" or "rare or special."

A. DIRECTIONS: *Rewrite each sentence so that it means the opposite of the original sentence by adding the prefix* un- *to one of the words in the original sentence. You will also have to change other words or the order of the words so that the new sentence makes sense.*

Original sentence:	A fact is something that is proven.
Sentence with opposite meaning:	An opinion is something that is *unproven*.

1. Lock the door when you leave the house.

_____

2. He had a warm, friendly smile.

_____

3. She studied hard and was prepared for the test.

_____

4. Fruits and vegetables are necessary foods in most diets.

_____

5. You need to fold the letter to put it in an envelope.

_____

B. DIRECTIONS: *Write C if the underlined vocabulary word is used correctly or I if it is used incorrectly. For each I sentence, write your own sentence showing the underlined word used correctly.*

____ 1. The dress was decorated with sparkling <u>sequence</u>.

_____

____ 2. The doctor used special tweezers to <u>extract</u> an eyelash from her eye.

_____

____ 3. <u>Organized</u> music is louder than piano music.

_____

____ 4. A bright orange hat is <u>essential</u> to most people's wardrobes.

_____

"Chicoria" adapted by José Griego y Maestas, retold by Rudolfo A. Anaya
from **"The People, Yes"** by Carl Sandburg
"Brer Possum's Dilemma" by Jackie Torrence
"John Henry" Traditional

Build Language Skills: Grammar

Commas

Use a **comma** in the following situations:

- before a conjunction that separates two independent clauses:
    Cats are my favorite pet, but my sister prefers dogs.
- between items in a series:
    We own a cat, a dog, and a hamster.
- after introductory words, phrases, or clauses:
    Yes, our cat is very shy and quiet.
    Walking on her soft paws, she rarely makes a sound.
- to set off appositives, participial phrases, or adjective clauses that interrupt a sentence:
    Bobo, our dog, is friendly.
    Bobo, welcoming us home, always expects a pat.
- to set off other parenthetical words and expressions that interrupt a sentence:
    Did you know, John, that our house caught fire?
    It was our cat, not our dog, that woke us up.

A. PRACTICE: *Insert one or more commas in each sentence, as needed.*

1. When I read I prefer humorous yarns.

2. Annie Oakley a famous sharpshooter appeared in one tale that I read.

3. I also read folk tales about Brer Possum Paul Bunyan and Pecos Bill.

B. Writing Application: *Expand each sentence according to the instructions in parentheses. Use commas where necessary.*

1. People enjoy all kinds of music. (Add an independent clause.) _____

_____

2. I like the singers Nanci Griffith and Natalie Merchant. (Add another singer.) _____

_____

3. I thought that song was beautiful. (Add an introductory clause that begins with *When.*)

_____

4. Those lyrics are in dialect. (Add an appositive to explain what *dialect* is.) _____

_____

"Brer Possum's Dilemma" by Jackie Torrence
"John Henry" Traditional
Selection Test A

Critical Reading *Identify the letter of the choice that best answers the question.*

____ 1. In "Brer Possum's Dilemma," what is the first thing that Brer Possum does for Brer Snake?
   A. He gets the snake out from under a brick.
   B. He helps the snake up from a deep hole.
   C. He puts the snake in a pocket.
   D. He helps warm the snake.

____ 2. In "Brer Possum's Dilemma," what does Brer Snake do after he gets into Brer Possum's pocket?
   A. He warms himself in the sun.
   B. He crawls back in the deep hole and puts the brick back on top of himself.
   C. He writes a thank-you note to Brer Possum for all the help he gave.
   D. He bites Brer Possum.

____ 3. Which word best describes Brer Possum in "Brer Possum's Dilemma"?
   A. helpful
   B. cruel
   C. sneaky
   D. self-pitying

____ 4. From his behavior, what can you conclude about Brer Snake in "Brer Possum's Dilemma"?
   A. He is loyal.
   B. He is very shy.
   C. He is fearful.
   D. He is deceitful.

____ 5. If you were writing a summary of "Brer Possum's Dilemma," which event would you most likely include?
   A. The story takes place back in the days when animals could talk.
   B. Brer Possum climbed a persimmon tree.
   C. Brer Snake asked Brer Possum for help.
   D. Brer Snake just hissed and hissed.

_____ 6. In the southern dialect of "Brer Possum's Dilemma," what does *Brer* mean?
   A. briar
   B. brother
   C. animal
   D. opossum

_____ 7. At the end of "John Henry," the hero is described as a "steel-drivin' man." What does this phrase mean?
   A. He hammers steel wedges into rock to help clear the way for building railroads.
   B. He drives trucks of steel and loads them onto railroad cars.
   C. He attaches one railroad car to another.
   D. He works as an engineer driving trains for the C. & O. Railroad.

_____ 8. What is the meaning of this stanza from "John Henry"?
   John Henry tol' his cap'n,
   Lightnin' was in his eye:
   'Cap'n, bet yo' las, red cent on me,
   Fo' I'll beat it to the bottom or I'll die,
   Lawd, Lawd, I'll beat it to the bottom or I'll die.'

   A. John Henry told his boss that he would beat the steam drill or die trying.
   B. John Henry told his boss that a lightning storm was coming but he could finish work first.
   C. Lightning came from John Henry's eye as he recalled his years at sea with the captain.
   D. John Henry told the captain that he would die that afternoon.

_____ 9. In "John Henry," who substitutes for the hero when he becomes sick?
   A. the shaker
   B. the machine
   C. Polly Ann
   D. all the above

_____ 10. After the hero of "John Henry" dies, what does the reaction of people in passing locomotives tell you?
   A. John Henry would soon be forgotten.
   B. John Henry was respected but not loved.
   C. People would long remember John Henry.
   D. John Henry was liked only by women.

____ 11. If you were summarizing "John Henry," which statement would you leave out?

A. John Henry foresees his own death when he is still a child.

B. The captain brings a steam drill to do John Henry's job.

C. The man who invented the steam drill thought he was mighty fine.

D. John Henry beats the steam drill but dies from his injuries.

____ 12. Which common feature of oral literature is found in "John Henry"?

A. repetition of words and phrases

B. use of dialect

C. a folk hero as the subject

D. all of the above

Vocabulary and Grammar

____ 13. Which word is an antonym for *commenced*?

A. attended

B. interrupted

C. ignored

D. ended

____ 14. A filing system helps make an office more _____.

A. organized

B. disorganized

C. essential

D. pitiful

____ 15. Where should commas be added in this sentence?

Brer Snake Brer Possum and John Henry are all characters from the oral tradition.

A. after *Snake* only

B. after *Snake* and *Possum*

C. after *Possum* only

D. nowhere; the sentence is correct as is

Essay

16. In a short essay, summarize the folk tale "Brer Possum's Dilemma." Tell what happens to the two main characters and which lesson you think one of them learns.

17. Write a brief essay about the character John Henry. Describe his appearance, talents, personality, and behavior.

"Brer Possum's Dilemma" by Jackie Torrence
"John Henry" Traditional
Selection Test B

Critical Reading *Identify the letter of the choice that best completes the statement or answers the question.*

____ 1. In "Brer Possum's Dilemma," what does Brer Snake ask Brer Possum to do?
   A. help him escape from under a brick
   B. help him get out of a deep hole
   C. put him in a pocket to warm him up
   D. all of the above

____ 2. In "Brer Possum's Dilemma," what is the likely reason that Brer Snake keeps asking for Brer Possum's help?
   A. He is too weak and injured to move.
   B. He is a lonely creature and wants Brer Possum's company.
   C. He wants to trick Brer Possum into coming close so that the snake can bite him.
   D. He is lazy and likes to get others to do his work.

____ 3. Which phrase best describes Brer Possum in "Brer Possum's Dilemma"?
   A. softhearted and unsuspicious
   B. caring but wary
   C. well-meaning but incompetent
   D. selfish but clever

____ 4. Which statement best summarizes "Brer Possum's Dilemma"?
   A. A kindhearted possum reluctantly helps a snake.
   B. A possum encounters a snake and suffers the consequences.
   C. A kindhearted possum reluctantly helps a snake and suffers the consequences.
   D. A snake who tries to be good cannot control his evil nature and finally bites a possum.

____ 5. Which sentence best states the theme, or generalization about life, of "Brer Possum's Dilemma"?
   A. Do not expect others to be kind to you just because you are kind to them.
   B. Opossums should stay away from snakes.
   C. Do not put a snake in your pocket, no matter what.
   D. Kindhearted people will never succeed in life.

____ 6. What is the effect of the southern dialect in "Brer Possum's Dilemma"?
   A. It retains the oral quality of the original.
   B. It adds authentic local flavor to the tale.
   C. It makes the speech more realistic.
   D. all of the above

____ 7. Which characteristic of oral literature is true of "Brer Possum's Dilemma"?
A. It was passed down by mouth before being written down.
B. It reveals aspects of the culture that produced it.
C. It teaches a lesson.
D. all of the above

____ 8. According to "John Henry," what does the title character do for a living?
A. He helps build railroads.
B. He repairs railroad tracks.
C. He designs tunnels for the railroads.
D. He is an engineer for the C. & O. Railroad.

____ 9. Which word best describes the title character of "John Henry"?
A. average
B. weak
C. lazy
D. stubborn

____ 10. Which statement best summarizes "John Henry"?
A. Steel driver John Henry asks his shaker to sing and pray as he tries to beat a steam drill.
B. Steel driver John Henry beats a steam drill but dies of the injuries he received.
C. John Henry was a steel-driving man in the late 1800s.
D. John Henry was an African American hero whose funeral was widely attended.

____ 11. In "John Henry," why does the title character try to beat the steam drill?
A. He is proud of his work and resents having a machine take it over.
B. He is a showoff who wants to show up his boss, whom his strongly dislikes.
C. He is trying to fulfill the vision he saw in childhood.
D. He is ambitious and wants his captain, or boss, to give him a raise.

____ 12. Why do you think "John Henry" includes the details about Polly Ann taking over for John Henry?
A. to show that John Henry's woman was a remarkable person, just as he was
B. to show that John Henry's job was an easy one that even a weak woman could perform
C. to show that John Henry's woman was not strongly troubled by his illness and death
D. to help explain how John Henry wins the contest

____ 13. From the details in "John Henry," what can you conclude about American life at the time it was written?
A. Train transportation was important.
B. People were taller than they are today.
C. Women performed the same jobs as men.
D. all of the above

Vocabulary and Grammar

___ 14. What would happen if a film *commenced*?
A. The audience would leave.
B. The audience would protest.
C. The lights would come on.
D. The movie house would become dark.

___ 15. In which sentence is the underlined word used correctly?
A. For the cash register to open, it is <u>essential</u> that you hit "Enter."
B. The seamstress sewed shiny <u>sequence</u> onto the gown.
C. An <u>organized</u> locker is a big mess.
D. <u>Extract</u> the tow truck to the car by using this thick metal chain.

___ 16. Where should commas be added in this sentence?
Singing songs helped workers pass the time maintain a steady pace and keep their spirits up.

A. after *songs* only
B. after *songs* and *time* only
C. after *time* and *pace* only
D. after *songs*, *time*, and *pace*

___ 17. Which sentence needs one or more commas added?
A. John Henry was a tall man by nineteenth-century standards.
B. John Henry competed with the steam drill, and everyone watched.
C. Fellow workers relatives and women from the West came to John Henry's funeral.
D. Because John Henry was considered a hero, people sang songs about him.

Essay

18. In a brief essay, state what you feel is the main theme, or message about life, in "Brer Possum's Dilemma." Then, show how the details of the tale point to that theme.

19. Retell the events of "John Henry" as a brief prose story. Use the events that appear in this tall tale and add others, if necessary.

"Western Wagons" by Stephen Vincent Benét; "Davy Crockett's Dream" by Davy Crockett; "Paul Bunyan of the North Woods" by Carl Sandburg

Vocabulary Warm-up Word Lists

Study these words from the selections. Then, complete the activities.

Word List A

amid [uh MID] *prep.* among; in the middle of
  Amid the crowd of angry people, John was the one voice of reason.

bellowing [BEL oh ing] *n.* the act of shouting loudly or roaring
  The stage manager kept on bellowing orders to the new actors.

blaze [BLAYZ] *v.* to establish by marking (as a trail)
  There were no roads, so the pioneers had to blaze their own trails.

kindled [KIN duhld] *v.* made something start burning
  We had kindled a fire, and soon the logs were burning.

mocking [MAHK ing] *adj.* making fun of or laughing at
  The hare spoke to the tortoise in a mocking voice.

reformed [ri FORMD] *v.* became changed for the better
  Last year, Rob skipped school a lot, but this year he has reformed.

revenge [ri VENJ] *n.* punishment for someone who has harmed you
  The people took revenge on the soldiers who invaded their land.

youngster [YUHNG ster] *v.* a young person
  Marla was only a youngster, but she was already a tennis star.

Word List B

continent [KAHN tuh nuhnt] *n.* one of Earth's seven large land masses
  Some pioneers crossed the American continent in a covered wagon.

fortune [FOR chuhn] *n.* luck; fate
  It was Donny's good fortune to have been found before dark.

gouged [gowjd] *v.* cut deeply or forced out with a thumb
  Carla accidentally gouged a hole in table with the knife.

griddle [GRID uhl] *n.* an iron plate used for on a stove top
  All morning, pancakes were cooking on the griddle.

legions [LEE juhnz] *n.* large numbers of people or things
  Legions of insects attacked the field and ate all the grain.

squatter [SKWAHT er] *n.* person living illegally on empty property
  Bill became a squatter in a house that had been empty for two years.

trifle [TRY fuhl] *n.* a little amount
  The song made her feel a sad, but just a trifle.

whirlwind [WERL wind] *n.* a windstorm that moves quickly
  The strong whirlwind brought down trees all over the city.

"Western Wagons" by Stephen Vincent Benét; **"Davy Crockett's Dream"** by Davy Crockett;
"Paul Bunyan of the North Woods" by Carl Sandburg

Vocabulary Warm-up Exercises

Exercise A *Fill in each blank in the paragraph below with an appropriate word from Word List A. Use each word only once.*

Ever since Horton was a [1] _____ of six, his dream was to

[2] _____ a trail through the jungle. Even though he was grown, he

could still hear the voices of the other kids [3] _____ him because they

thought his dream was silly. He never [4] _____, however, so that they

would approve of his future plans. Their taunts only [5] _____ a fire in

him to fulfill his dream. This year, as a graduate student in biology, he finally got sweet

[6] _____ on them. Now, he stood with a small group of explorers on the

dark floor of a rain forest [7] _____ trees whose tops he could not see. It

was much quieter and more peaceful than he had imagined. Not a single animal was

[8] _____. At last, he felt at home.

Exercise B *Revise each sentence so the underlined vocabulary word is used in a logical way. Be sure to keep the vocabulary word in your revision.*

1. It was the hare's good <u>fortune</u> to lose the race to the tortoise.

   _____

2. The <u>whirlwind</u> traveled quickly east up the middle of the <u>continent</u>.

   _____

3. We needed only one truck to carry the <u>legions</u> of soldiers to the waiting ship.

   _____

4. Touching a cold <u>griddle</u> is unwise and could hurt you a <u>trifle</u>.

   _____

5. On purpose, the carpenter <u>gouged</u> a deep hole in the beautiful table he had built.

   _____

6. The <u>squatter</u> wanted the police to know his new address.

   _____

"Western Wagons" by Stephen Vincent Benét; **"Davy Crockett's Dream"** by Davy Crockett;
"Paul Bunyan of the North Woods" by Carl Sandburg
Reading Warm-up A

Read the following passage. Pay special attention to the underlined words. Then, read it again, and complete the activities. Use a separate sheet of paper for your written answers.

Davy Crockett was a legend in his own time although he claimed he did not understand his fame. "I can't tell why it is, nor in what it is to end. Go where I will, everybody seems anxious to get a peep at me." You can almost hear his voice <u>mocking</u> himself. He had already become a war hero, a member of Congress, and a much-loved storyteller. He wasn't a loudmouth; no one could say they heard him <u>bellowing</u> all the time. Still, he was not one to keep his opinions to himself.

Davy's grandfather had been one of the first pioneers to <u>blaze</u> a trail through the mountains to what is now Tennessee. There, Davy was born in 1786 in a small cabin. While he was a <u>youngster</u>, he learned the skills required for life on the frontier. No doubt, he <u>kindled</u> many a fire to stay warm and hunted animals for food.

Growing up on the frontier, Davy also listened eagerly to travelers' tales, sparking his adventurous spirit. He left home at the tender age of twelve. In Virginia, he worked for farmers, wagoners, and a hat maker. He also became an expert with a rifle.

After fighting in the Creek Indian War in 1812–1813, Davy <u>reformed</u> some of his wilder ways. He became a member of the Tennessee State Legislature. Then, he went on to the United States Congress.

Adventure got the better of Davy, once again, however, and led to his most famous act. In the 1830s, Texas was part of Mexico. Settlers from the United States who had been moving in decided they wanted to be independent, and they set up their own country. The Mexican government, seeking <u>revenge</u>, sent its army to claim the land. A large army attacked a small group of Texans at the Alamo, a fort in San Antonio. When the battle was over, 187 Americans lay dead <u>amid</u> the 2,000 Mexican soldiers they had killed. Davy Crockett was among them.

1. Circle what Davy was <u>mocking.</u> Write a sentence using *mocking.*

2. Underline the two words that help you understand <u>bellowing</u>. Describe something you've heard *bellowing.*

3. Underline the phrase that tells what Davy's grandfather was the first to <u>blaze</u>. Explain *blazed.*

4. Circle the words in the next paragraph that help you understand the meaning of <u>youngster</u>. Tell something fun you can do as a *youngster.*

5. Circle the words that tell what Davy <u>kindled</u>. Write a sentence using *kindled.*

6. Circle the words that tell what Davy <u>reformed</u>. Write a sentence about how people with bad habits can be *reformed.*

7. Underline the words that explain how Mexico took <u>revenge</u>. Tell about another situation in which someone took *revenge.*

8. Underline the words that tell <u>amid</u> whom the dead Americans lay. Rewrite the sentence using a synonym for *amid.*

Name _____ Date _____

"Western Wagons" by Stephen Vincent Benét; **"Davy Crockett's Dream"** by Davy Crockett;
"Paul Bunyan of the North Woods" by Carl Sandburg
Reading Warm-up B

Read the following passage. Pay special attention to the underlined words. Then, read it again, and complete the activities. Use a separate sheet of paper for your written answers.

They called her Windy Wanda because she would blow into Hooten Hollow like a whirlwind, stir things up, and blow out again just as fast. At first, the townsfolk thought she was a squatter on some nearby land. Wanda, however, had left California, crossed half the continent, and paid for it with a gold nugget the size of Lake Tahoe.

Wanda cleared the forest around her house with an old hairpin. She gouged out holes in the ground with her boot nails and planted seeds. When thousands of locusts attacked her wheat crop, she fought off the legions of insects with a peashooter.

Now, to celebrate the wheat harvest, Hooten Hollow always had a flapjack-cooking contest. When Windy Wanda caught wind of that, she decided it would be no contest if she entered. She hooked up her team of twelve white horses in order to haul her griddle to town. It was the size of a swimming hole. She walked behind, carrying a butter churn. Behind her was a team of oxen pulling a covered wagon filled with flour. Next came twelve cows, each with a chicken clutching onto its back.

When the townsfolk spied Wanda, her animals, and her supplies coming down the road, they realized that she wanted to win the contest more than a trifle. Everybody scrambled out of her way. She began milking cows, churning butter with mind-boggling speed, and whispering to her chickens so they would lay eggs. She hollowed out a huge bowl in the earth to mix her batter. Then, she felled a tree with a hairpin, built a huge fire, and greased her griddle.

The townsfolk stood smiling at their good fortune as Wanda whipped up 1,212 flapjacks. Then, she gathered up her animals, her wagon, and her griddle. In as little time as it takes for a tornado to whip through town, Wanda and everything she had brought with her were gone.

1. Circle the words that show that Wanda is like a whirlwind. Explain how it might feel to be in a *whirlwind*.

2. Circle the phrase that describes something a squatter will never do. Tell about a place where a *squatter* might live.

3. Underline the word that hints at which half of the continent Wanda crossed. On which *continent* does the story take place?

4. Underline what Wanda gouged out. Then, write your own sentence for *gouged*.

5. Circle a word that tells what legions are. Of what would there be *legions* on a battlefield?

6. Circle the words that tell what it took to haul Wanda's griddle to town. How big is an ordinary *griddle*?

7. Tell how the townsfolk knew Wanda wanted to win more than a trifle. Tell about something that you want more than a *trifle*.

8. Circle the phrase that identifies the townsfolk's good fortune. Use the phrase *good fortune* in a sentence.

Name _____ Date _____

"Western Wagons" by Stephen Vincent Benét
"Davy Crockett's Dream" by Davy Crockett
"Paul Bunyan of the North Woods" by Carl Sandburg
Literary Analysis: Comparing Heroic Characters

Heroic characters are men and women who show great courage and overcome difficult challenges. A heroic character can be fictional or real. Often, the hero in a tall tale or legend is a combination of both—a real historical figure whose actions have become so exaggerated over time that he or she becomes a legend.

Many American legends and stories focus on the pioneers of the western frontier. Because survival in such a harsh setting depended on skill and strength, many tall tales and legends exaggerate these admirable qualities.

DIRECTIONS: *Answer the questions about each heroic character in the following chart.*

Questions	Pioneers in "Western Wagons"	Davy Crockett	Paul Bunyan
1. In what ways did the hero(es) show great courage?			
2. Did these characters overcome difficult challenges? How?			
3. What actions, if any, by the character(s) are exaggerated?			
4. Label the characters with one of these three phrases: real historical figure, fictional legend, or combination of both.			

"Western Wagons" by Stephen Vincent Benét
"Davy Crockett's Dream" by Davy Crockett
"Paul Bunyan of the North Woods" by Carl Sandburg
Vocabulary Builder

A. DIRECTIONS: *Answer each question in a sentence. Your answer must show you know the meaning of the italicized word.*

1. Would a camper want to have a fire *kindled* just before he or she packs up and leaves a campsite?

   _____

2. Would young business executives like to live in *shanties*?

   _____

3. If someone were *bellowing* at you, would you have trouble hearing him or her?

   _____

4. Would *squatters* want to be discovered living where they are by the police or the government?

   _____

5. During a movie, would you prefer for the people sitting in front of you to create a *commotion* or sit still?

   _____

B. DIRECTIONS: *For each related pair of words in CAPITAL LETTERS, circle the lettered pair that best expresses a similar relationship.*

1. SHANTIES : MANSIONS ::
   A. fire : cook
   B. glass : diamonds
   C. flower : spring
   D. construction : building

2. BELLOWING : ROARING ::
   A. needing : taking
   B. listening : talking
   C. sleeping : eating
   D. striving : laboring

3. KINDLED : FIRE ::
   A. bread : crust
   B. waited : left
   C. baked : cake
   D. match : oxygen

4. COMMOTION : ORDER ::
   A. compassion : indifference
   B. serious : humorless
   C. saddened : crying
   D. angry : mob

"Western Wagons" by Stephen Vincent Benét
"Davy Crockett's Dream" by Davy Crockett
"Paul Bunyan of the North Woods" by Carl Sandburg

Support for Writing to Compare Heroic Characters

Before you write your essay that compares and contrasts the way in which these three selections present heroic characters, use the graphic organizer below to list ideas about each character.

How does each writer use exaggeration? What is the effect?	"Western Wagons"	David Crockett	Paul Bunyan

How important is humor in each selection?	"Western Wagons"	David Crockett	Paul Bunyan

What do these legends show about the American character and what we admire in our heroes?	"Western Wagons"	David Crockett	Paul Bunyan

Now, use your notes to write an essay comparing and contrasting the presentations of the different heroic characters.

"Western Wagons" by Stephen Vincent Benét
"Davy Crockett's Dream" by Davy Crockett
"Paul Bunyan of the North Woods" by Carl Sandburg
Selection Test A

Critical Reading *Identify the letter of the choice that best answers the question.*

____ 1. In the poem "Western Wagons," what nationality are the people who are traveling west?
   A. Spanish
   B. American
   C. Dutch
   D. French

____ 2. Who is the speaker of the following line from "Western Wagons"?
   For I'm off to California to get rich out there or die!
   A. the poet himself
   B. Davy Crockett
   C. Columbus
   D. a pioneer

____ 3. How do the characters in "Western Wagons" show heroic courage?
   A. by taking a banjo and frying pan
   B. by taking land and settling it
   C. by crowding on the dusty trail
   D. by carrying their fortunes with them

____ 4. What challenges did the pioneers have to overcome according to "Western Wagons"?
   A. their wives and children
   B. packing kids and blankets
   C. starving, freezing, and suffering
   D. travelers passing by

____ 5. Which statement best summarizes the story "Davy Crockett's Dream"?
   A. While out hunting, Crockett and his dog get so cold that they take shelter in a shanty.
   B. A man named Oak Wing, whom Crockett injured five years earlier, takes revenge.
   C. While hunting, Crockett naps in a cabin, has a bad dream, and is awakened by his wife.
   D. Crockett's wife finds him in an old log cabin, where she pokes his eye out with an icicle.

___ 6. Why does Crockett have a hard time getting his hat off in the cold weather?
   A. He sweated, so the hat froze to his head.
   B. The cabin wasn't heated.
   C. The hat was too tight.
   D. He was too sleepy.

___ 7. In "Davy Crockett's Dream," why does Crockett want revenge on Oak Wing?
   A. because Oak Wing poked his eye out with an icicle
   B. because Oak Wing gave him an "almighty licking once"
   C. because he dreamt Oak Wing was pulling at his leg
   D. because he dreamt Oak Wing pounded him on his head

___ 8. Which line from "Davy Crockett's Dream" is an exaggerated statement?
   A. When I sneezed the icicles crackled all up and down the inside of my nose. . . .
   B. . . . I stood my rifle up agin one of the door posts and went in.
   C. . . . I took my little dog named Grizzle and cut out for Salt River Bay. . . .
   D. So I went and talked to him, and told him what he had done to me in a dreem. . . .

___ 9. Where did the stories about Paul Bunyan come from?
   A. lumberjacks
   B. bookless people
   C. people in shanties
   D. all of the above

___ 10. What can you infer about the Seven Axmen based on this passage?
   The commotion of the dancing that night brought on an earthquake and the Big Onion river moved over three counties to the east.

   A. The Seven Axmen were regular guys.
   B. The Seven Axmen were very large.
   C. The Seven Axmen were good dancers.
   D. The Seven Axmen wanted to move.

___ 11. Which of the following lines from "Paul Bunyan" is an exaggerated statement?
   A. He grew up in shanties, around the hot stoves in winter.
   B. Paul Bunyan got disgusted because his celebration on the Fourth was spoiled.
   C. Two mosquitoes lighted on one of Paul Bunyan's oxen, killed it, ate it, cleaned the bones.
   D. All the above.

___ 12. Which of the following statements from "Paul Bunyan" makes him seem heroic?

    A. Paul is old as the hills, young as the alphabet.

    B. Paul fixed a granite floor sunk two hundred feet deep.

    C. Seven Axmen had to dance with each other, the one left . . . taking Paul as a partner.

    D. He dived under this pillar, swam up into it, and climbed with powerful swimming strokes.

Vocabulary

___ 13. What might need to be kindled?

    A. a camper

    B. a fire

    C. a gas oven

    D. a cake

___ 14. Which word means the same as *commotion*?

    A. uproar

    B. distraction

    C. loud

    D. movement

___ 15. What type of people might live in *shanties*?

    A. elected officials

    B. well-to-do people

    C. military heroes

    D. poor people

Essay

16. Heroic characters are men and women who show great courage and overcome difficult challenges. In an essay, describe the heroic characters presented in "Western Wagons," "Davy Crockett's Dream," and "Paul Bunyan of the North Woods." How do these characters show courage? What difficult circumstances do they overcome? In your opinion, which character(s) showed the greatest heroism? Why?

17. As time passes, the actions of some legendary figures are sometimes exaggerated. Write an essay about exaggerations in "Western Wagons," "Davy Crockett's Dream," and "Paul Bunyan of the North Woods." First, give examples of the exaggeration, if any, in each work. Second, for each selection, identify its tone, or the attitude it takes toward its subject.

Name _____ Date _____

"Western Wagons" by Stephen Vincent Benét; **"Davy Crockett's Dream,"** by Davy Crockett;
"Paul Bunyan of the North Woods" by Carl Sandburg
Selection Test B

Critical Reading *Identify the letter of the choice that best answers the question.*

____ 1. In the poem "Western Wagons," the people traveling west are
   A. people moving to Los Angeles.
   B. nineteenth-century pioneers.
   C. Dutch and French.
   D. heroes of the Revolutionary War.

____ 2. What characteristic of the travelers is captured in this line from "Western Wagons"?
   We've broken land and cleared it, but we're tired of where we are.
   A. agricultural skill
   B. laziness
   C. curiosity
   D. restlessness

____ 3. What characteristic of the travelers is captured in this line from "Western Wagons"?
   We're going West tomorrow, where the promises can't fail.
   A. honesty
   B. bravery
   C. optimism
   D. competitiveness

____ 4. What value is expressed in this line from "Western Wagons"?
   But we're going West tomorrow, with our fortune in our hands.
   A. generosity
   B. cooperation
   C. self-reliance
   D. thoughtfulness

____ 5. Which line from "Western Wagons" shows that the travelers had great courage?
   A. They went with wife and children, in the prairie-schooner days.
   B. They say that wild Nebraska is a better place by far.
   C. And all across the continent the endless campfires glowed.
   D. We shall starve and freeze and suffer. We shall die, and tame the lands.

____ 6. What probably causes Crockett's dream in "Davy Crockett's Dream"?
   A. guilt for his treatment of Oak Wing
   B. discomfort in the cabin
   C. fatigue
   D. cold weather

____ 7. The best summary of "Davy Crockett's Dream" is that
   A. Crockett and his dog take shelter from the cold.
   B. Oak Wing, whom Crockett injured five years earlier, takes revenge.
   C. Crockett takes a nap, has a bad dream, and is awakened by his wife.
   D. Crockett's wife wakes him up.

____ 8. What happens later in "Davy Crockett's Dream" that proves the following statement to be true?

> . . . so that I could see when it was noon by the sun, for Mrs. Crockett was always rantankerous when I staid out over the time.

A. Crockett does not even fall asleep because he is too worried.
B. Crockett oversleeps, and Mrs. Crockett comes to find him.
C. Something falls down the chimney and hits Crockett in the head.
D. A cloud passes in front of the sun, and Crockett cannot judge the time.

____ 9. The line from "Davy Crockett's Dream" that is an exaggerated statement is
A. ". . . the wind went out of me and roared up chimney like a young whirlwind."
B. "I stood my rifle up agin one of the door posts and went in."
C. "I took my little dog named Grizzle and cut out for Salt River Bay to kill something. . . ."
D. "She said it was all a dreem and that Oak was not to blame. . . ."

____ 10. Which action from "Davy Crockett's Dream" shows that Crockett was courageous?
A. He goes hunting in the freezing cold.
B. He took a nap in a squatter's cabin.
C. He gouged out Oak Wing's eye.
D. He floats down a river in a hollow log.

____ 11. What does "Paul Bunyan of the North Woods" reveal about the storytellers who invented Bunyan and kept him alive in the oral tradition?
A. They needed a larger-than-life hero.
B. They told tales to see who was gullible.
C. They believed the stories were true.
D. They had seen such giants in real life.

____ 12. Which of these characteristics does *not* apply to "Paul Bunyan of the North Woods"?
A. The work is highly exaggerated.
B. The work is set on the American frontier.
C. The work is humorous.
D. The work has nothing to do with animals.

____ 13. After this line from "Paul Bunyan of the North Woods," how does Bunyan respond?

> One year when it rained from St. Patrick's Day till the Fourth of July, Paul Bunyan got disgusted because his celebration on the Fourth was spoiled.

A. Bunyan sulks about the weather.
B. Bunyan finds a way to stop the rain.
C. Bunyan tries to hide his disappointment.
D. Bunyan complains to his friends.

____ 14. Which line from "Paul Bunyan of the North Woods" is *not* an exaggerated statement?
A. He grew up in shanties, around the hot stoves in winter.
B. The Pacific Ocean froze over in the winter. . . .
C. Two mosquitoes lighted on one of Paul Bunyan's oxen, killed it, ate it. . . .
D. The barn was gone one morning and they found it on Benny's back. . . .

____ 15. A line that makes the main character of "Paul Bunyan of the North Woods" seem heroic is
   A. Paul fixed a granite floor sunk two hundred feet deep.
   B. . . . the one left over in each set taking Paul as a partner.
   C. Paul Bunyan got disgusted because his celebration on the Fourth was spoiled.
   D. . . . as the rain stopped, he explained, "I turned the darn thing off."

Vocabulary

____ 16. In which sentence is *kindled* used correctly?
   A. Derrick kindled the fire by pouring water over it.
   B. After setting up the tents, the campers kindled a fire to cook supper.
   C. The group gathered around the kindled and smoldering ashes of the fire.
   D. The blazing fire needed to be kindled before it got out of control.

____ 17. A synonym for *commotion* is
   A. uproar.
   B. distraction.
   C. loud.
   D. movement.

____ 18. Which of the following words is most *opposite* in meaning to *bellowing*?
   A. loud
   B. simple
   C. hushed
   D. angry

Essay

19. In an essay, compare and contrast the hero Davy Crockett with the hero Paul Bunyan. What heroic qualities does each have? What actions make each character heroic? How is each character exaggerated into a being larger than life? Was each character an actual historical figure or a fictional character?

20. Many American legends and stories focus on the pioneers of the western frontier. Write an essay comparing and contrasting the portrayal of pioneers in "Western Wagons" with the portrayal of Davy Crockett in "Davy Crockett's Dream" and the portrayal of Paul Bunyan in "Paul Bunyan of the North Woods." What challenges do the characters face? What heroic actions do the characters perform? How does exaggeration affect each selection? What is the tone of each selection?

21. Write a brief essay in which you discuss how you think each selection came to be. First, tell who wrote "Western Wagons." Where might the author of "Western Wagons" have gotten the information for the poem? Second, tell who wrote "Davy Crockett's Dream." How did that author probably get the idea for the story? Third, tell who wrote "Paul Bunyan of the North Woods." Where did the character called Paul Bunyan come from, according to this writer? Finally, tell what the three selections have in common.

Writing Workshop—Unit 6, Part 1
Research: Multimedia Report

Prewriting: Choosing Your Topic

List possible topics in the chart below. Then, select a subject that you know will have a range of multimedia material that is readily available to you.

Musicians or Artists	Films	Trends in Fashion or Hobbies	Professional Sports Teams

Drafting: Sketching an Outline

Before you begin to draft your actual text, develop an outline to shape your sequence of ideas by using the graphic organizer below.

Introduction: Address the topic and introduce the thesis statement or main idea in an innovative way.	
Body: Offer in-depth coverage of the topic and provide at least two examples— at least one of which should be conveyed in a medium other than text—to reinforce the thesis.	
Conclusion: Sum up research and restate the thesis.	

Writing Workshop—Unit 6, Part 1
Multimedia Report: Integrating Grammar Skills

Revising Run-on Sentences and Sentence Fragments

A **run-on sentence** is two or more complete sentences that are not properly joined or separated. A **sentence fragment** is a group of words that does not express a complete thought.

Sentence Errors	Corrected
Run-on: Charles is an avid reader he also is a dedicated athlete.	**Separate sentences:** Charles is an avid reader. He is also a dedicated athlete. **Comma and coordinating conjunction:** Charles is an avid reader, but he also is a dedicated athlete. **Semicolon:** Charles is an avid reader; he also is a dedicated athlete.
Fragment: By the next day.	**Corrected:** By the next day, she felt better.

Identifying Sentence Errors

A. DIRECTIONS: *Each pair below has a sentence error and a complete sentence. On the line, write* run-on, fragment, *or* sentence *to identify the item.*

1. A. Since Tonya plans to run for class treasurer. _____

   B. Since Tonya plans to run for treasurer, she will be campaigning.
   _____

2. A. The voting will be next week, so be sure to vote. _____

   B. The voting will be next week be sure to vote. _____

3. A. A meeting on Thursday, November 14, at 4 o'clock. _____

   B. The meeting will be on Thursday, November 14, at 4 o'clock. _____

Fixing Run-ons and Fragments

B. DIRECTIONS: *Write complete sentences to correct the run-ons and fragments.*

1. We are studying American history it is an interesting subject.

   _____

2. George Washington, a military leader.

   _____

3. Abraham Lincoln was the sixteenth president he gave a speech at Gettysburg.

   _____

4. After the assassination.

   _____

Unit 6: Themes in American Stories
Part 1 Benchmark Test 11

MULTIPLE CHOICE

Reading Skill

1. Which statement accurately describes a good summary?
   A. A good summary presents all the details that appear in the original work.
   B. A good summary is usually much longer than the original work.
   C. A good summary uses precisely the same phrases as the original work.
   D. A good summary restates a work's main ideas in as few words as possible.

2. Which statement below is the best summary of this paragraph?

   Among the huge number of things you can see at the Art Institute of Chicago are the Harding collection of medieval armor and the Thorne collection of miniature rooms, handmade to the smallest detail. The museum's paintings, which go back to the thirteenth century, include a particularly fine collection of European impressionist and post-impressionist works. The museum is also known for its American art and furniture, including the famous painting *American Gothic* by Grant Wood.

   A. The Art Institute of Chicago displays works going back to the thirteenth century.
   B. Highlights at the Art Institute of Chicago include a collection of medieval armor.
   C. The Art Institute of Chicago has a huge collection of works from Europe and America, stretching into the past and ranging from artifacts to paintings.
   D. At the Art Institute of Chicago you can find many famous works of art, including *American Gothic* by Grant Wood.

Read this selection from a story. Then, answer the questions that follow.

   Janine and I were out collecting specimens for a science project, though we were finding very few items that we needed. Suddenly, the sky grew dark and wind grew fierce. Realizing that a storm was coming, we turned and headed for home. We did not get far, however, when the downpour began. I ushered Janine into a cave on the side of the mountain to use as a shelter. Never having been in a cave, she was very frightened. The cave was damp and dark and smelled of decay. Luckily, we had a flashlight with us, though its light was rather dim. We remained there until the storm ended.

3. Which of these details should you probably include in a summary of the story?
   A. We had not found very many science specimens.
   B. During the storm, we found shelter in a cave.
   C. The cave was damp and dark and smelled of decay.
   D. Luckily we had a flashlight, though it was rather dim.

4. Which of these details should you probably *not* include in a summary of the story?
   A. Janine and I were collecting specimens for a science project.
   B. Janine and I had not found many specimens for our project.
   C. We went into a cave to find shelter from the storm.
   D. After the storm, we headed for home.

5. Which graphic aid would most help you organize a summary of this story?
   A. a time line
   B. a pie chart
   C. a cluster diagram
   D. a bar graph

6. Which of these types of writing is a good example of a summary?
   A. a description of a TV show in a TV guide
   B. a news story in a local or national newspaper
   C. the instruction manual that comes with a new automobile
   D. a story that appears in an anthology of short stories

Read this short book review. Then, answer the questions that follow.

(1) *Alice's Adventures in Wonderland* by Lewis Carroll is a delightful fantasy. (2) It tells of a young girl named Alice who follows a rabbit down a hole. (3) She has tea with a Mad Hatter and testifies at a trial of playing cards. (4) The book's greatest charm is in its creative depiction of a world far from reality. (5) However, some readers may have problems with dated details and unfamiliar British customs.

7. Which sentence in the review gives an overall opinion of the book?
   A. sentence 5
   B. sentence 4
   C. sentence 2
   D. sentence 1

8. Which two sentences in the review summarize the book?
   A. sentences 1 and 5
   B. sentences 2 and 3
   C. sentences 3 and 4
   D. sentences 4 and 5

9. Which two sentences in the review discuss the book's strengths and weaknesses?
   A. sentences 1 and 2
   B. sentences 2 and 4
   C. sentences 4 and 5
   D. sentences 3 and 5

Literary Analysis

10. For what main purpose did ancient peoples create myths?
    A. to create a body of literature that would stand the test of time
    B. to explain natural occurrences or events in the peoples' history
    C. to show that gods and goddesses are nothing like human beings
    D. to give enduring fame to heroes and heroines who contributed to the society

Name _____ Date _____

Read this ancient Greek myth. Then, answer the questions that follow.

Demeter, Greek goddess of agriculture, had a beautiful daughter named Proserpine. Pluto, god of the underworld and ruler of the dead, fell in love with Proserpina. When Demeter refused to permit their marriage, Pluto carried Proserpina off. After he married her, Demeter was filled with grief at the loss of her daughter. Finally Zeus, brother of Pluto and ruler of the gods, ruled that Proserpine should spend only part of the year with her husband. Each year when Proserpine went below ground, winter would come. When she rejoined her mother, spring would return.

11. What does the myth of Demeter and Proserpine show about the Greek gods and goddesses?
   A. They often display human qualities.
   B. They rarely display strong feelings or emotions.
   C. They are all very beautiful.
   D. They take little interest in human activities.

12. What does the myth of Demeter and Proserpine try to explain?
   A. the best way to grow grain
   B. the reason the underworld in dark
   C. the origin of bats
   D. the origin of the seasons

13. What does the behavior of Zeus in the myth suggest that the ancient Greeks valued?
   A. wealth
   B. unchecked power
   C. power guided by compassion
   D. respect for the dead

14. What does the myth of Demeter and Proserpine show about ancient Greek culture?
   A. People lived longer than they do today.
   B. Women had little influence over men.
   C. People lived in tiny, dark homes.
   D. Agriculture was an important activity.

15. What statement is true of literature composed in the oral tradition?
   A. It shows little about the culture that produced it.
   B. It is usually narrated in elegant formal English.
   C. It includes legends, songs, folk tales, and tall tales.
   D. It is usually written down soon after it is composed.

16. What is dialect?
   A. the conversations that characters have in a work of literature
   B. the language and grammar of a particular region or people
   C. the customs and values of a particular region or people
   D. works passed down by word of mouth before being written down

Read this selection from a legend told in the oral tradition. Then, answer the questions that follow.

Hijos, let me tell you a story from our long ago. It was a time when the rich *hidalgos* were cruel to the poor farmers. They worked them very hard and gave them very little. But one man, *un hombre*, he was a champion of the poor. This man, he was known as Zorro—The Fox. He stole from the rich and give to the poor. *El Señor* Zorro, he was bold and brave, and the finest swordsman in the world. No one could catch him. No one even knew who he was! That was because he wore a black mask over his eyes to keep his real identity hidden. Now I will tell you a secret, *mis hijos*. The real identity of this Zorro—he was a rich *hidalgo* himself! He became Zorro to make up for what other rich men did.

17. Which quality of this story most clearly suggests that it comes from the oral tradition?
    A. It uses formal, old-fashioned English.
    B. It uses lots of modern slang.
    C. It uses dialect and repetition.
    D. It explains what the name Zorro means.

18. Which statement best describes Zorro?
    A. He is a heroic character whose admirable qualities are exaggerated.
    B. He is a weak character who pretends to be strong in the face of evil.
    C. He is a selfish character who thinks very little about the feelings of others.
    D. He is a villainous character who upsets the social order in old California.

19. What does the popularity of the legend of Zorro show about the Spanish-American culture that produced it?
    A. It was a society with no economic or social classes.
    B. It was a society where crime was virtually unknown.
    C. It was a society where military might was deeply admired.
    D. It was a society where compassion for the poor was deeply admired.

20. From this retelling, what can you conclude that the Spanish word *hidalgos* means?
    A. aristocrats
    B. mayors
    C. farmers
    D. explorers

Vocabulary

21. Given the meaning of the prefix *dis-*, which paired items are the most *dissimilar*?
    A. a legend and a folk tale
    B. a god and a goddess
    C. a baseball and a noodle
    D. a stream and a river

22. Given the meaning of the prefixes *non-* and *un-*, which is a synonym of *nonessential*?
    A. uncertain
    B. unlimited
    C. unnecessary
    D. unthinkable

23. From your knowledge of prefixes, what do you think you call someone who does not behave in a conventional way?
    A. a nonresident
    B. a dishonor
    C. a uniform
    D. a nonconformist

24. In which sentence does the italic word make use of the prefix *an-* or *a-*?
    A. The World Series is an *annual* event in Major League Baseball.
    B. The government collapsed and complete *anarchy* followed.
    C. After she left public school, she enrolled in a private *academy*.
    D. When will they *announce* the winner of the contest?

Grammar

25. What type of sentence is this?

    During the boat trip down the Nile, the people saw several crocodiles.

    A. simple
    B. compound
    C. complex
    D. compound-complex

26. Which of these sentences is a compound sentence?
    A. For too long, Ms. Simmons paid little attention to the paperwork on her desk.
    B. When she finally approached the task, the pile of paperwork was enormous.
    C. She could do the work herself or hire a secretary.
    D. She inquired about a temporary secretary, but the cost was far too high.

27. How should this sentence be rewritten so that it uses commas correctly?

    Touring Spain we visited the cities of Madrid Granada, and Seville but never reached Barcelona.

    A. Add a comma after *Spain*, *Madrid*, and *Seville* and keep the comma after *Granada*.
    B. Add a comma after *Spain* and *Madrid* and remove the comma after *Granada*.
    C. Add a comma after *Madrid* and *Seville* only and keep the comma after *Granada*.
    D. Add a comma after *Spain* and *Madrid* and keep the comma after *Granada*.

28. How should you correct the punctuation in this sentence?

Owing to the rain the barbecue was canceled, our party was instead held indoors.

A. Add a comma after *rain* and remove the comma after *canceled*.

B. Add a comma after *rain* and change the comma after *canceled* to a semicolon.

C. Just change the comma after *canceled* to a period and capitalize the *o* in *our*.

D. No changes are necessary; the sentence is correct as is.

29. Which of these sentences is punctuated correctly?

A. The zoo which opens at ten stays open late on Thursdays, Saturdays, and Sundays.

B. Beautifully landscaped it is a large, impressive zoo with thousands of animals.

C. If you visit on a busy weekend, you will probably wait in line at opening time.

D. A visit usually costs seven dollars for adults but on Thursdays the zoo is free to all.

30. Which of these choices is a complete sentence?

A. The settlers building small cabins.

B. When they arrived in the New World.

C. Sailing for months across the Atlantic.

D. They traveled far.

ESSAY

Writing

31. Create a modern myth to explain something puzzling, annoying, or peculiar about modern life. For example, you might tell "Why the Bus Is Always Late" or "Why It Always Rains on Weekends." Make sure your myth tells how the specific aspect of life came to be.

32. Write a critical analysis of any work that features a heroic character. It might be a character you met in your reading, or it might be a hero or heroine from movies or TV. In your analysis, focus on how effectively the character is portrayed.

33. Imagine that you are writing a multimedia report on a myth. It might be a report on a natural phenomenon that the myth tries to explain or a report on a mythological character. Jot down your ideas for the elements you might include in your multimedia report and the information sources you might use to gather your information.

Unit 6 Resources: Themes in American Stories
104

Name _____

Starting Date _____ Ending Date _____

Unit 6: Themes in American Stories
Part 2 Concept Map

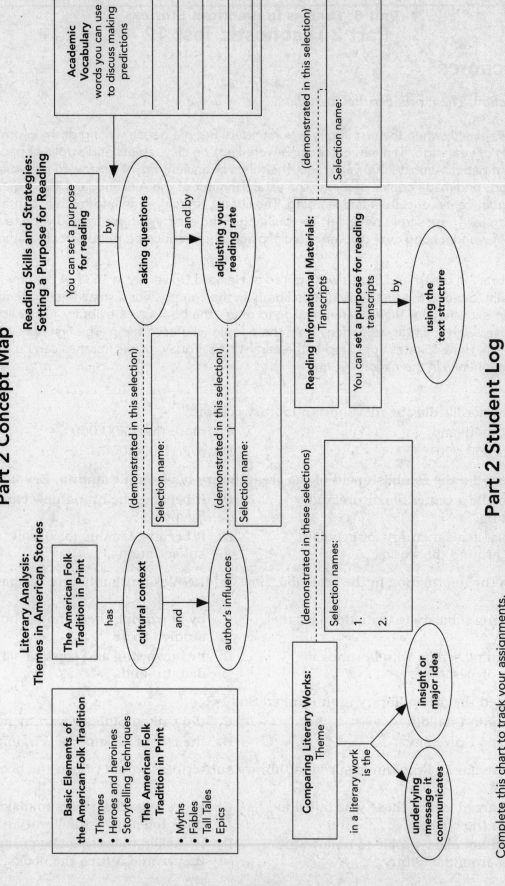

Literary Analysis: Themes in American Stories

The American Folk Tradition in Print — has → cultural context — and → author's influences

(demonstrated in this selection)
Selection name: _____

(demonstrated in this selection)
Selection name: _____

Basic Elements of the American Folk Tradition
- Themes
- Heroes and heroines
- Storytelling Techniques

The American Folk Tradition in Print
- Myths
- Fables
- Tall Tales
- Epics

Reading Skills and Strategies: Setting a Purpose for Reading

You can set a purpose for reading — by → asking questions — and by → adjusting your reading rate

(demonstrated in this selection)
Selection name: _____

Academic Vocabulary words you can use to discuss making predictions
_____
_____
_____

Reading Informational Materials: Transcripts

You can set a purpose for reading transcripts — by → using the text structure

Comparing Literary Works: Theme

in a literary work is the → insight or major idea

→ underlying message it communicates

(demonstrated in these selections)
Selection names:
1. _____
2. _____

Part 2 Student Log

Complete this chart to track your assignments.

Writing	Extend Your Learning	Writing Workshop	Other Assignments

Unit 6: Themes in American Stories
Part 2 Diagnostic Test 12

MULTIPLE CHOICE

Read the selection. Then, answer the questions.

No one knows exactly when the first library was founded. People began writing down information and ideas thousands of years ago. The earliest records were kept on clay tablets and scrolls of papyrus, a primitive form of paper. Almost 2000 years ago, the rulers of ancient Egypt borrowed papyrus scrolls from distant lands and made copies of them. The establishment of the Alexandrian Library made Alexandria, Egypt, a great center of culture and learning. The library, teeming with information, contained more than 700,000 scrolls. These scrolls never left the building. Scholars came from far and wide to study them. An aura of wonder hung over this very special place where educated people could gather to study and to teach.

The oldest library in the United States was started at Harvard University in 1638. A century later, Benjamin Franklin founded the first subscription library in the country. For a small fee, subscribers could borrow books in exchange for their solemn pledge to return the books to the library. Other libraries supported themselves with voluntary donations from the people who used them. The first tax-supported free libraries in the United States appeared in the early 1800s. Today, public libraries can be found in almost every community in the nation.

1. How many scrolls did the Alexandrian Library contain?
   A. a few thousand
   B. about 550,000
   C. more than 700,000
   D. over 1,000,000

2. What effect did the establishment of the great library have on Alexandria, Egypt?
   A. It became a center of culture and learning.
   B. It became a sanctuary for scholars from around the world.
   C. It became the brand new capital of Egypt.
   D. It became famous for use of subscriptions.

3. Based on the information in the selection, how did the Alexandrian library get many of its scrolls?
   A. by hiring scholars to write them for the library
   B. by trading scrolls with libraries in other places
   C. by borrowing them from scholars who studied there
   D. by borrowing and copying scrolls from distant lands

4. Who started the oldest library in the United States?
   A. Benjamin Franklin
   B. Harvard University
   C. the United States government
   D. the city of Alexandria, Virginia

5. How did Benjamin Franklin ensure that library subscribers would return the books they borrowed?
   A. He charged fees of those who failed to return the books.
   B. He did not allow people to remove the books from the library.
   C. He asked subscribers to make donations to support the library.
   D. He asked them to make promise that they would return the books.

6. Most community libraries today are funded by tax dollars. If you connect this information to details in the selection concerning the history of American libraries, what conclusion can you draw about how early American libraries were funded?
   A. Donations and small fees were not enough to support them.
   B. People did not want their taxes increased to pay for libraries.
   C. People did not value libraries very much in the early days.
   D. The ones that were supported by taxes were not successful.

7. What is the main idea of this selection?
   A. Libraries are centers of learning and culture.
   B. The history of libraries is long and fascinating.
   C. There was a great library in ancient Alexandria, Egypt.
   D. American libraries tried many ways of supporting themselves.

Read the selection. Then, answer the questions.

Imagine a wall of brick and stone, fifteen feet wide and twenty-five feet high. Imagine that it spans some fifteen hundred miles. That's roughly the distance from New York City to Omaha, Nebraska. Imagine a wall so vast that astronauts orbiting Earth can see it from space! Believe it or not, you've just imagined one of the seven wonders of the world—the Great Wall of China.

Built entirely by hand, the Great Wall was begun around the 7th century BCE. It took many hundreds of years to complete. The first segments were built thousands of years ago to keep out invaders from the north. Nearly paralyzed by the fear of being overrun by barbarians, Chinese emperors ordered that a wall be built in order to protect the people.

When nomadic Mongols entered the country through gaps in the wall, the emperors ordered more walls built to fill in the gaps. Millions of laborers were enlisted to help at the bustling work sites that sprang up across the country.

Today, people come from all over the world to walk along the Great Wall and marvel at its beauty. Protecting the ancient Wall from damage without halting tourism has been an ongoing concern for the Chinese government.

8. What is the purpose of the first paragraph in the selection, in which the writer asks the reader to imagine the Great Wall of China?
   A. to persuade readers to visit the Great Wall of China
   B. to argue for the protection and preservation of the wall
   C. to hook readers' attention with visual images of the wall
   D. to compare the Great Wall to other wonders of the world

9. What are the measurements of the Great Wall?
   A. 5 feet wide, 15 feet high, and 1000 miles long
   B. 15 feet wide, 25 feet high, and 1500 miles long
   C. 25 feet wide, 50 feet high, and 2500 miles long
   D. 50 feet wide, 100 feet high, and 3000 miles long

10. What is a unique feature of the Great Wall of China compared to other ancient structures?
    A. It is built of brick and stone.
    B. It was built entirely by hand.
    C. It took a very long time to complete.
    D. It is so large it can be seen from space.

11. Why was the Great Wall built?
    A. to protect China from barbarian invaders
    B. to make Chinese emperors feel important
    C. to create something that could be seen from space
    D. to have a tourist attraction that would last for centuries

12. How long did it take to complete the Great Wall?
    A. about ten years
    B. over 100 years
    C. many hundreds of years
    D. thousands of years

13. What effect did Mongol invasions have on the building of the wall?
    A. They slowed down the wall building for centuries.
    B. They finally brought the building of the Great Wall to a stop.
    C. They caused the emperors to speed up building to close the gaps.
    D. They did not affect the building of the Great Wall in any significant way.

14. Why did it take so long to complete the Great Wall?
    A. It was built entirely by hand.
    B. There were many worker rebellions.
    C. Emperors kept getting distracted.
    D. Invaders repeatedly destroyed the wall.

15. What detail from the selection supports the idea that the modern Chinese government is experiencing conflict about the Great Wall?
    A. Mongols entered the country through gaps in the wall.
    B. They want to protect the wall without ending tourism.
    C. The Great Wall is huge and can be seen from space.
    D. Early Chinese emperors were terrified of barbarians.

Vocabulary Warm-up Word Lists

Study these words from the poetry of Joseph Bruchac. Then, complete the activities.

Word List A

knowledge [NAHL ij] *n.* understanding; learning
   Everyone in our family has <u>knowledge</u> of camping.

memory [MEM uh ree] *n.* something remembered from the past
   My father has no <u>memory</u> of the first house he lived in.

native [NAY tiv] *adj.* referring to the place one is born
   Is Spanish or English your <u>native</u> language?

sickness [SIK nuhs] *n.* disease; illness; bad condition
   They suffered from the <u>sickness</u> for only two days

slips [SLIPS] *v.* moves smoothly and quietly
   After the boat <u>slips</u> up to the dock, we tie it to a post.

veins [VAYNZ] *n.* tubes in the body through which blood flows
   Blood for testing is taken from <u>veins</u> near the surface of the arm.

Word List B

answerer [AN ser er] *n.* someone or something that answers
   We hoped the new government would be an <u>answerer</u> of our needs.

decades [DEK aydz] *n.* a period of ten years
   A century is made up of ten <u>decades</u>.

empires [EM pyrz] *n.* individual or groups of countries, often made up of diverse people, with a single ruler, such as an emperor
   The Austrian and Turkish <u>empires</u> were defeated in World War I.

invaded [in VAYD id] *adj.* entered so as to take over
   China was <u>invaded</u> by the Japanese military in the 1930s.

quarantine [KWAHR uhn teen] *n.* a time when someone or something is kept apart from others so as to prevent the spread of any possible disease
   We waited anxiously until our dog's <u>quarantine</u> ended.

Slovak [SLOH vahk] *adj.* native to, living in, or descended from Slovakia, a country in central Europe
   The <u>Slovak</u> capital is Bratislava, a city on the Danube River.

"Ellis Island" by Joseph Bruchac
Vocabulary Warm-up Exercises

Exercise A *Fill in each blank in the paragraph below with an appropriate word from Word List A. Use each word only once.*

The rowboat [1] _____ quietly through the water, nearing the shore. Looking back, one of the sailors sees the ship getting smaller and smaller. The pulse of excitement runs through the sailor's arteries and [2] _____. None of his shipmates has any better [3] _____ than he has of the land they are about to explore. Will they meet any [4] _____ peoples in the new land? Will they be friendly or hostile? The sailor's [5] _____ of his last landfall remains strong. The crew was unprepared for the rough greeting they received. A small military force drove them back to their ship. "Is it a [6] _____ to want to explore new territory?" he wonders. "If it is, then it is an illness of the most wonderful kind."

Exercise B *Decide whether each statement below is true or false. Circle T or F, and explain your answers.*

1. Some <u>decades</u> are longer than others.
   T / F _____

2. <u>Empires</u> were more common in the past than today.
   T / F _____

3. A country that has been <u>invaded</u> could be a dangerous place.
   T / F _____

4. It is a sensible thing to break <u>quarantine</u>.
   T / F _____

5. There are no <u>Slovak</u> people living in the United States.
   T / F _____

6. If you refused to give someone something they wished for, you would be an <u>answerer</u>.
   T / F _____

Name _____ Date _____

"Ellis Island" by Joseph Bruchac
Reading Warm-up A

Read the following passage. Pay special attention to the underlined words. Then, read it again, and complete the activities. Use a separate sheet of paper for your written answers.

When I came to this country, I felt reborn. Still, I feel it is important to preserve every underline{memory} I can of the old country to pass something along to my children—and their children. Why do I feel that I need to hold on to things from my past? I will try to explain it to you.

I move among American-born residents of this city, knowing that my story is very different from theirs. I will never take this country for granted. I can't shake the underline{knowledge} of the horrible things my underline{native} country's government did to its people in the name of security.

In America, I no longer fear arrest or torture. I no longer fear for my life. In underline{sickness} or in health, I will be able to live peacefully here, and I will not be thrown into the gutter if I become too ill to work or even stand up. I will pass along to my children the gift of freedom that will rush through their underline{veins} along with their blood.

Now and again, in a moment of quiet, a memory of the old country underline{slips} through my mind. It is noiseless, like muffled paddles rowing smoothly across the water of a calm lake. A picture of the old life sometimes comes into my mind's eye, but it never seems to have any words. If it did what words would it have—those of my native language or those of English?

"Get on with your life," people tell me, and I do. I don't live in the past, nor do I want to. Still, I do not want to stop remembering the past. The moment I do, the reasons that brought me here would lose their grip. I might become like some Americans who, born in the U.S.A., take the country for granted.

1. Circle the words that suggest the meaning of underline{memory}. Write about a *memory* you have.

2. Underline the underline{knowledge} that the author cannot shake. Tell about some *knowledge* you would rather not have.

3. Circle the word in the paragraph that contrasts with the author's underline{native} country. Tell about the place to which you are *native*.

4. Circle the word that is the opposite of underline{sickness}. Write about a time you had to stay home because of *sickness*.

5. Underline the two things that the author imagines flowing through his children's underline{veins}. Describe your *veins* based on what you can see.

6. Underline the words in the next sentence that identify what the author compares with a memory that underline{slips} through his mind. Explain how a memory *slips* through one's mind.

Name _____   Date _____

"Ellis Island" by Joseph Bruchac
Reading Warm-up B

Read the following passage. Pay special attention to the underlined words. Then, read it again, and complete the activities. Use a separate sheet of paper for your written answers.

For almost six <u>decades</u>, beginning after the Civil War, millions of immigrants arrived on America's shores. Many were escaping the harsh rule and lack of freedom in the <u>empires</u> of southern, central, and eastern Europe. Many were escaping the crushing poverty of rural life. Some were escaping both.

Those nearly sixty years in American history were marked with great changes. The population of eastern cities swelled with Greeks, Italians, Jews, Poles, Romanians, and Russians. Swedish and Norwegian found their own pieces of land in the Midwest and West. Nearly seven of every ten <u>Slovak</u> men became coal miners in the South. Many languages unfamiliar to Americans were being spoken and new customs were being practiced across the land.

Immigration was hardly ever easy, even though organizations helped newcomers. Crossing the ocean by ship was hard. Sometimes, an arriving ship was placed under <u>quarantine</u> if officials feared an outbreak of a serious illness that could come ashore.

Also, once on American soil, people often had difficulties communicating and getting along. In everyday business, a questioner and an <u>answerer</u> might need a person to translate. One group might mistrust another.

Then, in 1924, the government passed the Johnson-Reed Act. This law set up limits, to the number of immigrants who could enter the United States from different countries. It favored people from northern Europe. The effect was terrible on people living in other countries that had been <u>invaded</u> by foreign armies.

Despite everything, many people believe that the United States has benefited from immigration. Today, immigrants come from many countries in addition to Europe. Many still come to America for the same reasons—to find freedom and a chance for a better life.

1. Circle the phrase in the next paragraph that means the same as "for almost six decades." Write a sentence about an event that happened during one of the last two *decades*.

2. Underline the words that identify where the <u>empires</u> were. Explain what *empires* are.

3. Circle the word that tells who was <u>Slovak</u>. Write a sentence using *Slovak*.

4. Underline the words that help you figure out the meaning of <u>quarantine</u>. Describe what it might be like to live under *quarantine*.

5. Circle the word that is an antonym of <u>answerer</u>. Describe a situation when someone is an *answerer*.

6. Underline the words that help you understand the meaning of <u>invaded</u>. How would you feel if the United States were *invaded*?

Name _____ Date _____

"Ellis Island" by Joseph Bruchac
Reading: Ask Questions to Set a Purpose for Reading

Setting a purpose for reading helps you focus your attention as you read a literary work. One way to set a purpose is to **ask questions** about the topic of the work, questions that you can answer as you read. Using the K-W-L chart can help you to ask questions that can be answered by reading the work. Consider this example using "Ellis Island":

"K" What I already know about the topic: I know that Ellis Island was the site at which hundreds of thousands of European immigrants entered the United States in the late 1800s and early 1900s.	"W" What I want to know: I want to know what kinds of experiences people had while they were at Ellis Island.	"L" What I learned: I will answer this question after I have read the poem.

DIRECTIONS: *Read each passage from "Ellis Island" below. As you read, think about what you knew before you read the poem and what you learn from reading the poem. Then, write an answer to each question.*

> Beyond the red brick of Ellis Island
> where the two Slovak children
> who became my grandparents
> waited the long days of quarantine,

1. What kinds of experiences did people have at Ellis Island?

_____

> Yet only one part of my blood
>   loves that memory.
> Another voice speaks
> of native lands
> within this nation.

2. What other historical context plays a role in the writer's personal background?

_____

"Ellis Island" by Joseph Bruchac
Literary Analysis: Cultural Context

The **cultural context** of a literary work is the social and historical environment in which the characters live. Major historical events such as a war or bad economic times can shape people's lives in important ways. As you read, look for details that show how characters respond to cultural and historical events. Consider the following passage from "Ellis Island":

> Beyond the red brick of Ellis Island
>
> where the two Slovak children
>
> who became my grandparents
>
> waited the long days of quarantine,

The poet describes the entrance of two of his grandparents into the United States. They entered Ellis Island from the part of Europe that is now called Slovakia. At Ellis Island, they had to wait in quarantine to be checked for illnesses that could infect the people already living in America. The cultural context here is an important historical event—the massive immigration of people into the United States.

DIRECTIONS: *Read the passage from "Ellis Island," and answer the questions.*

> Yet only one part of my blood
>
>   loves that memory.
>
> Another voice speaks
>
> of native lands
>
> within this nation.
>
> Lands invaded
>
> when the earth became owned.
>
> Lands of those who followed
>
> the changing Moon,
>
> knowledge of the seasons
>
> in their veins.

1. To whom does the author refer as his other immigrant ancestors, besides those who came from Slovakia?

   _____

2. What does the poet tell readers about Native American people?

   _____

   _____

3. What is the major cultural context of this poem? Explain your answer.

   _____

   _____

Name _____ Date _____

"Ellis Island" by Joseph Bruchac
Vocabulary Builder

Word List

native   quarantine

A. DIRECTIONS: *For each item below, think about the meaning of the italicized Word List word, and then answer the question.*

1. If a person were *native* to Sweden, would he or she be called a German? Explain.

   _____

2. If you were in *quarantine* with the measles, could you visit your friends? Why or why not?

   _____

3. Does an immigrant continue to live in his or her *native* land? Explain.

   _____

4. If people are put into *quarantine* with a contagious illness, is the illness likely to spread to others not in *quarantine*? Why or why not?

   _____

B. DIRECTIONS: *For each item, decide which choice has the meaning that is closest to the numbered word.*

1. native
   A. strange
   B. local
   C. current
   D. ordinary
2. quarantine
   A. illness
   B. health
   C. standing
   D. isolation

Name _____ Date _____

Support for Writing a Research Proposal

To prepare a **research proposal** for a report on immigrant experiences passing through Ellis Island in the 1890s and early 1900s, use the Internet and library resources and enter data into the chart below.

Research Proposal on Ellis Island Immigration Report	
Three questions about immigrants and their experiences at Ellis Island	_____ _____ _____ _____ _____ _____
Three sources that contain information to answer the above questions	_____ _____ _____ _____ _____ _____
Points to make in proposal	_____ _____ _____ _____ _____ _____ _____ _____

On a separate page, write a draft of your research proposal. Include a description of the sources you found, and explain why they will be useful.

"Ellis Island" by Joseph Bruchac
Support for Extend Your Learning

Research and Technology

As you gather information for your **letter** as an immigrant writing to a friend in the "old country," enter important information, images, emotions, and other details of your experiences at Ellis Island in the chart below. Use information from the previous page, if you wish.

Information for Letter to Friend	
Experiences I had at Ellis Island	
Images (sounds, sights, tastes) I can share from Ellis Island	
My emotional responses to experiences at Ellis Island	

Listening and Speaking

As you work in a small group to prepare an **oral presentation** on Ellis Island and immigration in America history, complete the activities below:

- Collect visuals—photographs, illustrations, documents—on immigration through Ellis Island.
- Read diaries and journals of Americans who came to the United States through Ellis Island.
- Find statistics on the numbers of people who came through Ellis Island, where they came from, and when.

Prepare your oral presentation from the information you have collected.

"Ellis Island" by Joseph Bruchac
Enrichment: An Immigration History

Ellis Island was named for Samuel Ellis who owned it in the 1770s. It served as the port of entry for immigrants coming to America from 1892 to 1954. During its peak years, Ellis Island processed some 12 million immigrants. They came from countries all over the world. Some were escaping political and religious problems. Others sought better economic opportunities. All came seeking a better way of life.

Today, Ellis Island serves as a public museum under the direction of the National Park Service. Where immigrants once waited to be medically examined, tested, and processed, their descendants now walk through the halls learning about their ancestors' experience.

The first great wave of immigration (1840s–1850s) consisted of about 4 million Irish people escaping the potato famine in Ireland. About 4 million Germans came from the 1840s to the 1880s, fleeing from economic depression and political unrest. From the 1870s to the 1890s, about $1\frac{1}{2}$ million Scandinavians came looking for farming opportunities. The years 1880 through the 1920s brought large numbers of groups— Poles, Austrians, Czechs, Hungarians, Slovaks, and Italians—fleeing poverty and overpopulation—as well as Eastern European Jews fleeing religious persecution.

DIRECTIONS: *Answer the following questions using the information above.*

1. Ellis Island processed immigrants from 1892 to 1954. How many years was it open? _____

2. If four million Irish immigrants came to the United States from the years 1840 to 1859, about how many came each year? _____

3. During which years would Joseph Bruchac's European grandparents have come to the United States? _____

4. In the early 1900s, the average cost of a steamship ticket for an immigrant was $30. If a ship held 1,500 immigrant passengers, how much money did the ship owner collect? _____

Name _____ Date _____

"Ellis Island" by Joseph Bruchac
Selection Test A

Critical Reading *Identify the letter of the choice that best answers the question.*

____ 1. If reading a selection can help you answer questions about a topic, how might you set a purpose for reading that selection?
   A. Watch a video about the topic.
   B. Ask questions about the topic.
   C. Write the author about the topic.
   D. Take a test about the topic.

____ 2. At the beginning of the poem "Ellis Island," why do the poet's grandparents have to wait in quarantine?
   A. Their papers are being checked.
   B. They are getting sent back home.
   C. They are being studied for disease.
   D. They are studying to be doctors.

____ 3. Which of these describes a cultural context of the poem "Ellis Island"?
   A. The poet comes from two backgrounds.
   B. The poet has visited Ellis Island.
   C. The poet has not owned land.
   D. They poet has seen the Statue of Liberty.

____ 4. In "Ellis Island," the poet writes that a ship "slips easily on its way to the island of the tall woman." Who is the "tall woman"?
   A. the immigration director
   B. the Statue of Liberty
   C. his grandmother from Slovakia
   D. the doctor who examines immigrants

____ 5. In "Ellis Island," to whom is the poet referring when he says "Another voice speaks of native lands within this nation"?
   A. the voice of his Slovak grandparents
   B. the voice of immigrants at Ellis Island
   C. the voice of his family
   D. the voice of Native Americans

_____ 6. Who are the poet's grandparents in "Ellis Island"?
   A. Native Americans only
   B. Native Americans and Slovaks
   C. immigration officials and Slovaks
   D. Slovaks only

Vocabulary and Grammar

_____ 7. In which sentence is the meaning of the word *quarantine* expressed?
   A. The officials count the immigrants as they leave the ship.
   B. The immigrants are kept separate while their health is checked.
   C. Large crowds meet the ships full of immigrants.
   D. Officials interview immigrants about their backgrounds.

_____ 8. In which sentence is the meaning of the word *native* expressed?
   A. The immigrants left the land of their birth.
   B. My grandparents speak three languages.
   C. The immigrant ship unloaded slowly.
   D. We visited Europe for the holidays.

_____ 9. Which of the following sentences correctly uses a semicolon?
   A. She has dogs; he has cats.
   B. She has dogs he; has cats.
   C. She has; dogs he has cats.
   D. She; has dogs he has cats.

_____ 10. Which of the following sentences needs a semicolon to connect the two parts of the sentence?
   A. People sailed by the State of Liberty, and they docked at Ellis Island.
   B. People sailed by the State of Liberty and docked at Ellis Island.
   C. People sailed by the State of Liberty before they docked at Ellis Island.
   D. People sailed by the State of Liberty they docked at Ellis Island.

Essay

11. Like many Americans, the poet of "Ellis Island" has two groups of ancestors. How might these groups think and feel about each other, based on what is said in the poem? How does this difference affect the poet? Write a brief essay that explains the main difference between the two groups.

Name _____ Date _____

"Ellis Island" by Joseph Bruchac
Selection Test B

Critical Reading *Identify the letter of the choice that best completes the statement or answers the question.*

____ 1. If reading a selection enables you to answer questions about a topic, which purpose might you set for reading that selection?
    A. preparing a report on the topic
    B. making a film about the topic
    C. completing a test about the topic
    D. asking questions about the topic

____ 2. In "Ellis Island," why do the poet's Slovak grandparents have to wait in quarantine?
    A. People from Slovak countries were usually ill.
    B. All immigrants had to be checked for disease.
    C. They were waiting to be met by relatives in the United States.
    D. They had come to America without the proper papers.

____ 3. What is the main cultural context of "Ellis Island"?
    A. The poet longs to visit European empires.
    B. The poet has Native American and European ancestors.
    C. The poet has visited Ellis Island for over nine decades.
    D. The poet works on a Circle Line ship.

____ 4. In "Ellis Island," what is "the answerer of dreams" in these lines?
    Like millions of others,
    I too come to this island,
    nine decades the answerer
    of dreams.

    A. Slovakia
    B. the Circle Line ship
    C. the Statue of Liberty
    D. Ellis Island

____ 5. What does the poet of "Ellis Island" mean by the phrase "native lands within this nation"?
    A. Europeans formed their own communities in America.
    B. Native American people welcomed the new Americans.
    C. Many people from different nations came to live in America.
    D. Europeans formed a nation where native people had lived.

____ 6. What does the poet of "Ellis Island" mean by the lines "Lands invaded / when the earth became owned"?
    A. His Slovak grandparents took the land of his Native American grandparents.
    B. His Slovak grandparents joined the army that invaded Native American lands.
    C. European immigrants took the land of Native Americans.
    D. European immigrants rented land from the Native Americans.

____ 7. Which cultural practice of Native Americans is referred to in this passage?

Lands of those who followed

the changing Moon,

knowledge of the seasons

in their veins.

A. moving from place to place

B. creating stories about the moon

C. honoring animals

D. predicting the weather

Vocabulary and Grammar

____ 8. In which sentence is the meaning of the word *native* expressed?

A. Mr. Wu's homeland is China.

B. Mr. Wu immigrated to the United States.

C. Mr. Wu settled in New York City.

D. Mr. Wu runs a chain of restaurants.

____ 9. In which sentence is the meaning of the word *quarantine* expressed?

A. Immigrants with illnesses were separated from others.

B. Immigrants waited to meet their U.S. relatives.

C. Immigrants were given information about housing.

D. Immigrants often traveled in large family groups.

____ 10. In which of the following sentences is the semicolon used correctly?

A. Many countries sent immigrants to America early settlers came from Scotland; Ireland; and England.

B. Many countries sent immigrants to America; early settlers came from Scotland, Ireland, and England.

C. Many countries; sent immigrants to America, and early settlers came from Scotland, Ireland, and England.

D. Many countries sent immigrants; to America; early settlers came from Scotland, Ireland, and England.

Essay

11. In "Ellis Island," how do the views of European immigrants and Native Americans toward Ellis Island differ? Write a brief essay to explain this difference. Use examples from the poem to support your explanation.

12. Based on "Ellis Island," contrast the views of European immigrants and Native Americans regarding the idea and value of owning land. Write a brief essay, using evidence from the poem to support your ideas.

Vocabulary Warm-up Word Lists

Study these words from Out of the Dust. *Then, complete the activities.*

Word List A

brewing [BROO ing] *v.* getting ready to happen soon
    Looking at all of those dark clouds, I think a storm is <u>brewing</u>.

dampen [DAM puhn] *v.* to make something slightly wet
    Before you iron, you can use a spray bottle to <u>dampen</u> the clothes.

fleeing [FLEE ing] *v.* leaving quickly, usually to escape danger
    A shark was spotted, so people were all <u>fleeing</u> from the ocean.

harvest [HAHR vist] *n.* the act of gathering ripe crops
    In many farming towns, the <u>harvest</u> means hard work and celebration.

relief [ri LEEF] *n.* the happy feeling you have when something bad has ended or not happened
    I sighed with <u>relief</u> when there was no pop math quiz today.

stumbled [STUHM buhld] *v.* almost fell while walking
    Too many people have <u>stumbled</u> over that crack in the sidewalk.

Word List B

drought [DROWT] *n.* a long period of very dry weather, causing a water shortage
    During the <u>drought</u>, we had two hundred days without any rain.

feuding [FYOOD ing] *n.* fighting over a long period of time
    My brothers love <u>feuding</u> about who will get the bathroom first.

locomotive [loh kuh MOH tiv] *n.* a train engine that can push or pull the cars
    We sat in the first car of the train, just behind the <u>locomotive</u>.

rickety [RIK uh tee] *adj.* in bad condition and likely to break
    The <u>rickety</u> porch swing did not seem safe to me.

sparse [SPAHRS] *adj.* small in number and spread over an area
    From the airplane I saw the <u>sparse</u> houses dotting the hilly landscape.

spindly [SPIND lee] *adj.* so long and thin as to appear weak
    The water bug walked on <u>spindly</u> legs across the pond's surface.

from **Out of the Dust** by Karen Hesse
Vocabulary Warm-up Exercises

Exercise A *Fill in each blank in the paragraph below with an appropriate word from Word List A. Use each word only once.*

It was a clear morning in late fall, just after the [1] _____. A few cars sat in the huge parking lot of the state fair. Still, a feeling of excitement dangled in the air, the knowledge that something big was [2] _____.Within two hours, things had gotten very busy in the lot—and very hot. I was constantly using a wet towel to [3] _____ my forehead and neck. Suddenly, I noticed a crowd spilling out of the gates of the fair. They seemed to be frightened and were [4] _____ from something. Several people [5] _____, and I was afraid someone would get hurt in the rush. With [6] _____, I watched a dozen security guards arrive and start to bring order to the somewhat wild crowd. "Had a bull gotten loose?" I wondered.

Exercise B *Answer the questions with complete explanations.*

1. Can a train move without a <u>locomotive</u>?

   _____

2. Would a very old table with <u>spindly</u> legs be likely to be <u>rickety</u>?

   _____

3. Why might a terrible <u>drought</u> lead to food shortages?

   _____

4. What makes <u>feuding</u> different from having an argument?

   _____

5. Why are plants <u>sparse</u> in a desert area?

   _____

from **Out of the Dust** by Karen Hesse
Reading Warm-up A

Read the following passage. Pay special attention to the underlined words. Then, read it again, and complete the activities. Use a separate sheet of paper for your written answers.

In the 1930s, major problems were <u>brewing</u> for small farmers in the United States. They were finding it harder and harder to make money. The government did step in with aid. The troubles did not stop, however. By the 1970s, millions of American farmers had given up. Families that had farmed generations were <u>fleeing</u> to cities to find jobs.

As a result, much farming today looks more like a big business. Farming companies use huge new tractors and other machines that are very expensive. Such equipment allows the work to be done on very large areas of land. During <u>harvest</u>, for example, these machines churn out the crops at high speeds and with little waste. How can a small farmer without modern equipment compete?

Many Americans have noticed the loss of small farms. They want to reverse the process. As the United States Department of Agriculture (USDA) has said: "[Small farms] are a unique part of our heritage, a tradition older than the nation itself, and a national treasure that must be preserved . . . bigger is not necessarily better."

Farmers in the twenty-first century have welcomed with <u>relief</u> the new help offered by the USDA. Since 1998, the USDA has been working to reach 146 goals. These have been set to help America's small farmers and ranchers succeed.

Many Americans shop in ways that support the small farmer. They stop at roadside stands to buy fruits and vegetables. They ask their stores to offer locally grown foods. Some shoppers have even <u>stumbled</u> through the fields at small "pick your own" farms. Americans seem to be willing to pay a bit more for food grown by small farmers.

Perhaps you have seen pictures of proud American farmers hard at work. The sweat of their labors may <u>dampen</u> their clothes but not their spirits.

1. Underline the words naming the group for whom problems were <u>brewing</u>. Then, explain what *brewing* means.

2. Circle the words explaining why farmers were <u>fleeing</u> to cities. Then, describe another time when people were seen *fleeing* from a bad situation.

3. Underline the words telling what modern machines do during a <u>harvest</u>. Then, explain what happens during *harvest*.

4. Circle the words naming the group that has felt <u>relief</u>. Then, tell about a recent time when you felt *relief*.

5. Underline the words naming where some people have <u>stumbled</u>. Then, explain why the visitors might have *stumbled* in these areas.

6. Underline the words identifying what <u>dampens</u> the farmers' clothes. Then, write a sentence using *dampen*.

from **Out of the Dust** by Karen Hesse
Reading Warm-up B

Read the following passage. Pay special attention to the underlined words. Then, read it again, and complete the activities. Use a separate sheet of paper for your written answers.

Have you ever heard of the Dust Bowl? No, it is not an important college football game but an area in the United States. People no longer call this area, in the western Great Plains states where the population is <u>sparse</u>, the Dust Bowl. However, in the 1930s, all of the grass and topsoil were gone from the land, and winds created constant dust storms.

There were years of <u>drought</u> throughout the plains, and the lack of rain contributed to the situation. In addition, farmers in the area did not take proper care of the soil. At first, the land produced great crops, but without fertilization and enough time to rest, it soon sent forth only a few <u>spindly</u> stems. When grass and topsoil are stripped away in these ways, nothing but dust remains.

As the situation got worse, people began <u>feuding</u> over the few plots of good land that were left. Many people became very poor, even to the point of starvation. They had to leave the area, often moving farther west to California in search of jobs and a better life.

Photographs from the time show thin, desperate people with a few pieces of <u>rickety</u> furniture loaded onto wagons. Always, the Dust Bowl families appear dirty, covered with a layer of dust. Where a <u>locomotive</u> was once heard chugging through the plains several times a day, trains no longer came and went through the deserted towns.

Since the 1930s, the area has been replanted with grass and trees. Reservoirs have been built, assuring a constant supply of water to irrigate the land.

1. Underline the word naming what is <u>sparse</u> in the Great Plains states. Then, explain what *sparse* means.

2. Circle the words in the next sentence that tell what causes a <u>drought</u>. Then, describe a *drought*.

3. Underline the phrase giving two reasons why the land could produce only <u>spindly</u> plants. Then, tell what a *spindly* plant would look like.

4. Circle the words naming what people began <u>feuding</u> over. Then, describe how people act and feel when *feuding*.

5. Underline the word that tells what was <u>rickety</u>. Describe something else that might be *rickety*.

6. Circle the word in the sentence that gives a good clue about the meaning of <u>locomotive</u>. Describe the sound a *locomotive* would make.

from **Out of the Dust** by Karen Hesse

Reading: Ask Questions to Set a Purpose for Reading

Setting a purpose for reading helps you focus your attention as you read a literary work. One way to set a purpose is to **ask questions** about the topic of the work, questions that you can answer as you read. Use a K-W-L chart to ask questions, and then answer them. See the example below, using material from *Out of the Dust.*

"K" What I already know about the topic: I know that the Dust Bowl during the Great Depression made farming life on the Great Plains almost impossible.	"W" What I want to know: How did people keep going when their crops were so often destroyed in the Dust Bowl?	"L" What I learned: I will answer this question after I have read the selection.

DIRECTIONS: *Read each passage from* Out of the Dust, *and then answer each question.*

Debts
Daddy is thinking
of taking a loan from Mr. Roosevelt and his men,
to get some new wheat planted
where the winter crop has spindled out and died.
Mr. Roosevelt promises
Daddy won't have to pay a dime
till the crop comes in.

1. What is one solution the Roosevelt administration set up to help farmers?

_____

Migrants
We'll be back when the rain comes,
they say,
pulling away with all they own,
straining the springs of their motor cars.
Don't forget us.

And so they go,
fleeing the blowing dust . . .

2. What did some Dust Bowl farmers do instead of trying to grow another wheat crop?

_____

Name _____ Date _____

from **Out of the Dust** by Karen Hesse
Literary Analysis: Cultural Context

The **cultural context** of a literary work is the social and historical environment in which the characters live. Major historical events can shape people's lives in important ways. Consider this passage from *Out of the Dust:* "While Ma and Daddy slept, / the dust came, / tearing up fields where the winter wheat, / set for harvest in June, / stood helpless. / I watched the plants, / surviving after so much drought and so much wind, / I watched them fry . . ."

This passage describes the onset of a dust storm, narrated by a character who lived in the Dust Bowl in the 1930s. The Dust Bowl era, in which failed crops led to poverty and hunger, is the historical context of the passage.

DIRECTIONS: *Read this example from* Out of the Dust, *and answer the questions.*

> Daddy says, / "I can turn the fields over, / start again. / It's sure to rain soon. / Wheat's sure to grow."
>
> Ma says, "Bay, / it hasn't rained enough to grow wheat in / three years."
>
> I ask Ma / How, / After all this time, / Daddy still believes in rain.
>
> "Well, it rains enough," Ma says, / "now and again, / to keep a person hoping. / But even if it didn't / your daddy would have to believe. / It's coming on spring, / And he's a farmer."

1. How do the father and mother respond to the event that rules their lives?

   _____

   _____

2. According to the mother, why does the father continue to hope for rain?

   _____

   _____

from **Out of the Dust** by Karen Hesse
Vocabulary Builder

Word List

| feuding   spindly   drought   sparse   rickety |

A. DIRECTIONS: *For each item below, think about the meaning of the italicized Word List word, and then answer the question.*

1. Would you expect a pair of *feuding* brothers to live together? Why or why not?
   _____

2. Does a hippopotamus or a rhinoceros have *spindly* legs? Explain.
   _____

3. Is a *drought* a good period in which to plant vegetables and flowers? Why or why not?
   _____

4. Would you expect the hair on a newborn baby to be *sparse*? Explain.
   _____

5. Is a *rickety* stepladder one that needs repair before you use it? Explain.
   _____

B. DIRECTIONS: *For each item, decide which choice means the **opposite** of the numbered word.*

1. feuding
   A. quarreling
   B. forgiving
   C. questioning
   D. puzzling

2. spindly
   A. shaky
   B. painted
   C. safely
   D. thick

3. drought
   A. rainstorm
   B. blizzard
   C. earthquake
   D. tornado

4. sparse
   A. extra
   B. rebellious
   C. plentiful
   D. limited

5. rickety
   A. weak
   B. dirty
   C. polished
   D. sturdy

from **Out of the Dust** by Karen Hesse
Support for Writing a Research Proposal

To prepare a **research proposal** for a report on how farmers in the 1930s were affected by the Dust Bowl, use the Internet and library resources, and enter data into the chart below.

Research Proposal on Dust Bowl Report	
Three questions about the Dust Bowl and its effects on farm families	_____ _____ _____ _____ _____ _____
Three sources that contain information to answer questions	_____ _____ _____ _____ _____
Points to make in proposal	_____ _____ _____ _____ _____ _____

On a separate page, write a draft of your research proposal. Include a description of the sources you found, and explain why they will be useful.

from **Out of the Dust** by Karen Hesse
Support for Extend Your Learning

Research and Technology

As you gather information for your **letter** as a migrant worker in California to a friend back in Oklahoma, enter important information, images, emotions, and other details of your experiences in the chart below. Use information from the previous page, if you wish.

Information for Letter to Friend	
My experiences in Dust Bowl Oklahoma	_____ _____ _____ _____
Images (sight, sound, touch) from Dust Bowl Oklahoma	_____ _____ _____ _____ _____
My emotional response to experiences in Oklahoma	_____ _____ _____ _____

Listening and Speaking

As you work in a small group to prepare an **oral presentation** on what it was like to live in Dust Bowl Oklahoma, complete the activities below:

- Collect visuals—photographs, illustrations, documents—on living as farmers in Oklahoma during the 1930s
- Read diaries and journals of farmers and family members who lived in Dust Bowl Oklahoma
- Find statistics on the number of farmers who farmed the Great Plains during the 1930s and the number who went to other states to become migrant workers.

Prepare your oral presentation from the resources you have collected.

from **Out of the Dust** by Karen Hesse
Enrichment: Into the Dust

Karen Hesse's descriptions of dust storms and their effects on the land and people are striking. Life on the Plains during the years of the drought and the dust storms was frightening. But oddly enough, people got used to it. Children accepted it as normal to wear dust masks to and from school. Plains wives came to accept covering their windows and doors with blankets and rugs as a regular activity. Plains farmers learned to harvest thistles for food when their wheat crops failed.

When the wind blew from the south it brought dust that was yellowish-brown. From the north, the dust blew in walls of black. The April 14, 1935, dust storm was the worst recorded, and came to be called the "Black Blizzard." The day was remembered afterward as "Black Sunday."

A dust storm could reach 2 miles high, extend for over 100 miles on the ground, and travel at 50 miles per hour. Not even fast-flying birds could not escape a fast-moving storm. People stayed inside if at all possible, though dust coated everything. They wore wet sponges over their faces. They used wet sacks as a form of vacuum cleaner, waving the sacks through the air to "sweep" away the dust.

Drought and poor farming practices led to the Dust Bowl years. Plowing the prairie for crops had loosened the ground cover that was thousands of years old and that held the soil in place. Repeated planting further loosened the soil. After the drought years, new planting practices were put in place. But thousands of farms had been lost, and thousands of farm families had lost their livelihoods.

DIRECTIONS: *Choose a weather event that you have experienced. This can be a blizzard, a thunderstorm, a heavy rain, a tornado or other form of windstorm, or a hurricane. Write a short piece to communicate to readers what living through this storm was like, just as Karen Hesse does in* Out of the Dust. *Use figurative language that helps readers see, hear, and feel the storm and its effects. If you need more room, use another sheet of paper.*

_____

_____

_____

_____

_____

_____

_____

_____

_____

"Ellis Island" by Joseph Bruchac
from **Out of the Dust** by Karen Hesse
Build Language Skills: Vocabulary

Borrowed and Foreign Words

Many words in English come from Native American languages. For example, *squash* comes from an Algonquian word *askutasquash*, which means "vegetables eaten green."

A. DIRECTIONS: *Look below at each Native American word and its meaning. Then, decide which English word is the best match and write it in the blank.*

| barbecue | chipmunk | chocolate | bayou | raccoon |

1. *bayuk*: from the Choctaw, meaning "small stream" _____
2. *barboca*: from the Haitian, meaning "framework of sticks" _____
3. *atchitamon*: from the Ojibwa, meaning "head first" (describing the way the animal goes down a tree trunk) _____
4. *arahkun*: from the Algonquian, meaning "scratches with his hands" _____
5. *chocolatl*: from the Nahuatl, meaning "bitter water" _____

Academic Vocabulary Practice

| critique | skim | focus | identify | revise |

B. DIRECTIONS: *Rewrite each sentence so that the italicized word is used in a way that makes sense. Be sure to include the italicized word in your new sentence.*

1. My teacher liked my report, so I had to *revise* it several times.

   _____

2. The actress was pleased by the negative *critique* of her performance.

   _____

3. I closed my eyes so I could *focus* on the picture.

   _____

4. It took all afternoon for me to *skim* the story to find the theme.

   _____

5. These blurry photos will help the woman *identify* her friend from college.

   _____

"Ellis Island" by Joseph Bruchac
from **Out of the Dust** by Karen Hesse
Build Language Skills: Grammar

Semicolons and Colons

Use a **semicolon (;)** to join independent clauses that are not already joined by the conjunctions *and, but, or, nor, for, so,* or *yet.*

> The ship passed the Statue of Liberty and sailed to the pier at Ellis Island.

> The ship passed the Statue of Liberty; it docked at the pier on Ellis Island.

Use a **colon (:)** to set off a list of items that follow an independent clause.

> The immigrants came from a variety of European countries: Ireland, Germany, England, France, and Russia.

A. DIRECTIONS: *Decide whether each of the following sentences needs a semicolon or a colon. Insert each punctuation mark where it belongs. You will not need to change the punctuation of every sentence.*

1. Immigrants come to American for several reasons many are looking for economic opportunity.

2. The young boy took his favorite items out of his trunk photographs of his family, a cap knitted by his grandmother, and a small telescope.

3. The immigrants spoke many languages, so they could not communicate with each other.

4. Each immigrant was examined by a doctor those who were healthy were cleared to go.

5. The immigrant family unwrapped their lunch potato pie, cheese, and apples.

B. DIRECTIONS: *Write a short paragraph about one of your grandparents or an older person in your family. Use at least one sentence with a semicolon and one sentence with a colon in your paragraph.*

_____

_____

_____

_____

_____

_____

_____

_____

_____

Name _____ Date _____

from **Out of the Dust** by Karen Hesse
Selection Test A

Critical Reading *Identify the letter of the choice that best answers the question.*

____ 1. In setting a purpose for reading the selection from *Out of the Dust,* which question would you ask?
A. Where did Dust Bowl farmers learn their farming techniques?
B. How much did wheat sell for during the years of the drought?
C. For how many seasons did the family plant a wheat crop?
D. How did Dust Bowl farmers deal with the drought and dust?

____ 2. In the selection from *Out of the Dust,* how are the wheat plants affected by the dust storm?
   I.   They burn up.
   II. They are flattened.
   III. They are eaten by birds.
   IV. They are blown away.
A. I, II, III
B. II, III, IV
C. I, III, IV
D. I, II, IV

____ 3. What can you conclude based on *Out of the Dust* that describes what the narrator does during the dust storm?
A. Nothing stops the dust.   C. Ma and Daddy sleep through it.
B. Lightning comes with the dust.   D. Trains stop the dust.

____ 4. What is the main cultural context of *Out of the Dust*?
A. the loss of neighbors who move away
B. the effect of the storms on families
C. the necessity of having a working car
D. the importance of loans to Plains farmers

____ 5. What is the major disagreement between Ma and Daddy in this selection from *Out of the Dust*?
A. They disagree about raising children.
B. They disagree about how to plant wheat.
C. They disagree about hoping for rain.
D. They disagree about getting a loan.

____ 6. What does the narrator of the selection from *Out of the Dust* say will bring the migrants back to the community where she lives?

    A. a new car

    B. the return of rain

    C. a new source of income

    D. a different strain of wheat

____ 7. In the selection from *Out of the Dust,* what does the writer mean when she describes the wheat as "sparse as the hair on a dog's belly"?

    A. It only comes up to the belly of a dog.

    B. There is very little wheat growing.

    C. Eating wheat will not fill a dog's belly.

    D. Dogs do not eat wheat to survive.

____ 8. What can you conclude from the section of *Out of the Dust* that mentions the migrants leaving?

    A. There is more fun in Arkansas and Texas.

    B. Their cars will only get to Arkansas or Texas.

    C. Their relatives live in Arkansas and Texas.

    D. There is more rain in Arkansas and Texas.

____ 9. What question is answered by the selection from *Out of the Dust*?

    A. What are the names of the narrator's parents?

    B. What was life like for Dust Bowl families?

    C. How long did the Dust Bowl drought last?

    D. How many families became migrant farmers?

____ 10. Which parts of the selection from *Out of the Dust* help you to identify the historical context?

    I.   the author's name

    II. the headings

    III. the reference to Roosevelt's loans

    IV. the description of a dust storm

    A. I, III, IV

    B. I, II, IV

    C. II, III, IV

    D. I, II, III

___ 11. Based on the selection from *Out of the Dust,* during what historical period did the Dust Bowl take place?

    A. the 1950s Cold War

    B. the 1940s World War II

    C. the 1930s Depression

    D. the 1890s Reform Era

Vocabulary and Grammar

___ 12. In which sentence is the meaning of the word *drought* expressed?

    A. I heard the wind rise, and stumbled from my bed.

    B. While Ma and Daddy slept, the dust came.

    C. We'll be back when the rain comes, they say . . .

    D. "Daddy!" I called. "You can't stop dust."

___ 13. Which of the following sentences correctly uses a colon?

    A. The people of the Depression fought hard against many things: dust, drought, and hopelessness.

    B. The people of the Depression fought hard against many things, dust: drought, and hopelessness.

    C. The people of the Depression: fought hard against many things, dust, drought, and hopelessness.

    D. The people of the Depression fought hard: against many things, dust, drought, and hopelessness.

Essay

14. In the selection from *Out of the Dust,* how does the narrator help the reader to experience life in the Dust Bowl? What kinds of language does she use to communicate this experience? Write a brief essay to give your ideas. Use at least two examples from the selection to support them.

15. How might the Dust Bowl experience reflected in *Out of the Dust* have shaped the narrator's cultural ideas? Write a brief essay to suggest ways in which the narrator's personality and beliefs would have been affected by living through such a time.

from **Out of the Dust** by Karen Hesse
Selection Test B

Critical Reading *Identify the letter of the choice that best completes the statement or answers the question.*

____ 1. Which of these questions would help you set a purpose for reading the selection from *Out of the Dust*?
   A. Who was president during the Dust Bowl years?
   B. How did the Dust Bowl affect farmers in the area?
   C. What is the land like today in the Dust Bowl area?
   D. How did snow affect the land in the Dust Bowl?

____ 2. What is the cultural context of *Out of the Dust*?
   A. The Great Depression
   B. The Civil War
   C. The World War II Years
   D. The Vietnam Era

____ 3. Which of these is a purpose you could set for reading the selection from *Out of the Dust*?
   A. to learn about different strains of wheat
   B. to learn about farming in the Dust Bowl
   C. to learn about migrant workers
   D. to learn about Roosevelt's administration

____ 4. Which meteorological condition is a major cause of the Dust Bowl?
   A. blizzard
   B. drought
   C. rain
   D. hurricane

____ 5. What does this description from *Out of the Dust* suggest about the way a dust storm behaves?
   > It wasn't until the dust turned toward the house,
   > like a fired locomotive,

   A. It focuses only on buildings.
   B. It moves along railroad tracks.
   C. It comes on schedule.
   D. It is fast-moving and loud.

____ 6. In *Out of the Dust*, what do the narrator's words, "Daddy, you can't stop dust!" tell you about how she responds to the historical event of the dust storms?
   A. She laughs at the bad events.
   B. She ignores the bad events.
   C. She is realistic about the bad events.
   D. She plans to flee the bad events.

_____ 7. Which of these questions can you answer after reading the first section of the selection from *Out of the Dust?*
A. What does a dust storm feel and sound like?
B. How many dust storms are there in a given year?
C. How often do Dust Bowl families clean their homes?
D. Who wins the argument between Ma and Daddy?

_____ 8. What keeps the Dust Bowl father from giving up in the selection from *Out of the Dust?*
A. His daughter loves their home.
B. He gets loans from the government.
C. His wife does not want to leave.
D. He has faith in the coming rain.

_____ 9. In the selection from *Out of the Dust*, why might Ma have a more realistic outlook about their chances at farming than Daddy?
A. She knows more about farming than he does.
B. She has lived here longer than he has.
C. She keeps the financial records for the farm.
D. She is expecting another child to feed.

_____ 10. In the selection from *Out of the Dust*, which of these contributes to the cultural context of the father's faith in farming?
A. When spring comes, a farmer has hope.
B. He gets news of rain from other farmers.
C. He has not farmed long enough to despair.
D. Farmers know wheat does not need much rain.

_____ 11. Which of these questions can be answered after reading the section from *Out of the Dust* headed "March 1934—Migrants"?
A. Do the migrants ever come back?
B. Where are the migrants going?
C. How many people leave the Dust Bowl?
D. Who takes care of the migrants' land?

_____ 12. In the selection from *Out of the Dust*, what can you assume about Texas and Arkansas after reading the section "March 1934—Migrants"?
A. There are empty farms there.
B. The rainfall is more common there.
C. The migrants' relatives live there.
D. The roads are in better shape there.

_____ 13. Which of these describes the way many farmers probably think in the selection from *Out of the Dust?*
A. They are used to disappointment.
B. They get angry at little things.
C. They have faith in the government.
D. They regret their choice of farming.

____ 14. Which of these character traits is part of the cultural character of the migrants in the selection from *Out of the Dust*?
A. They are careful about their decisions.
B. They do not care about their lives.
C. They will change their lives if they must.
D. They do not listen to their children.

Vocabulary and Grammar

____ 15. In which sentence is the meaning of the word *feuding* expressed?
A. The dust storm tears the wheat to pieces.
B. Daddy keeps hoping that the rain will come.
C. Ma and Daddy disagree.
D. The migrants seek better conditions elsewhere.

____ 16. In which sentence is the meaning of the word *rickety* expressed?
A. The dust storm sounds like a fired locomotive.
B. Ma cleans and cleans but the dust comes back.
C. The goat cages aren't sturdy enough for the trip.
D. Daddy tries but fails to save the wheat plants.

____ 17. Which of the following sentences correctly uses a colon?
A. Daddy came in: and sat across from Ma, blowing his nose that was filled with mud.
B. The narrator's parents were thinking: about getting a loan from the government.
C. The farmers did everything they could: pushed rugs against doors, dampened rags, and wiped dust.
D. The new winter wheat crop: had grown spindly and died.

____ 18. Which of the following sentences needs a colon in order to be written correctly?
A. Farmers held onto hope they planted, watched, and hoped.
B. The narrator writes about experiences such as her family, their farm, and her feelings.
C. The people of the Dust Bowl fought everything; dust, drought, and despair.
D. Even the houses fought the terrible dust—windows, doors, and roofs were helpless.

Essay

19. Do you think it was healthy or unhealthy for the farmer in the selection from *Out of the Dust* to continue to have faith that rain would come? Write a brief essay giving your ideas. Use details from the selection to support your ideas.

20. Based on the selection from *Out of the Dust*, what do you think it was like to live in a Dust Bowl home? Write a brief essay to compare what you think it was like with the kinds of environmental or weather situations we have today.

21. How does a selection such as *Out of the Dust* help readers to see what poverty is like for people who live in specific historical and cultural times? What did you learn about the economy of the Great Depression from reading this selection? What issues of poverty are you familiar with that can be compared with the economic situation of the Dust Bowl?

Vocabulary Warm-up Word Lists

Study these words from "Choice: A Tribute to Dr. Martin Luther King, Jr." Then, complete the activities.

Word List A

capable [KAY puh buhl] *adj.* having the skill needed to do something
   It surprised us that Jane was capable of doing cartwheels.

cemetery [SEM uh ter ee] *n.* a place where dead people are buried
   After the funeral service, Grandpa was buried in the cemetery.

fearless [FEER lis] *adj.* not afraid of anything
   When it comes to trying new sports, John is surprisingly fearless.

heritage [HER uh tij] *n.* the beliefs, values, and traditions of a group
   On national holidays, people celebrate their rich heritage.

importance [im PORT uhns] *n.* the quality of being meaningful
   The outcome of the Civil War had great importance to our country.

inherited [in HER it id] *v.* received something after someone has died
   My mother inherited a diamond necklace from her grandmother.

resistance [ri ZIS tuhns] *n.* standing firm against others' actions
   The citizens showed resistance to cooperating with the invaders.

rotted [RAHT id] *v.* crumbled away from natural decay
   After many years of neglect, the wooden house rotted away.

Word List B

abandonment [uh BAN duhn muhnt] *n.* the leaving behind
   The abandonment of the mill marked the end of cloth production.

acknowledge [ak NAWL ij] *v.* to accept that something is true
   It is important to acknowledge one's strengths and weaknesses.

ancestral [an SES truhl] *adj.* relating to family members of long ago
   Our ancestral home in Russia was destroyed in World War II.

birthplace [BERTH plays] *n.* the place where someone is born
   If you return to your birthplace, you will see little has changed.

brutality [broo TAL i tee] *n.* cruel actions
   The citizens suffered much brutality at the hands of the invaders.

handcuffed [HAND kuhft] *adj.* with the wrists placed in metal rings
   The guards surrounded the handcuffed prisoner.

municipal [myoo NIS uh puhl] *adj.* relating to city government
   Because the city is broke, it is cutting municipal services.

realities [ree AL uh teez] *n.* events that are real or truths
   Some people do not like to face the harsh realities of life.

141

"Choice: A Tribute to Dr. Martin Luther King, Jr." by Alice Walker
Vocabulary Warm-up Exercises

Exercise A *Fill in each blank in the paragraph below with an appropriate word from Word List A. Use each word only once.*

Antonio's family was from the "old school." Long after they arrived in America, they kept alive their [1] _____, which connected them with their family's roots. On every holiday, older family members told about the [2] _____ of keeping traditions alive. They believed that each generation [3] _____ much more than material goods. Traditions such as holiday gatherings and visiting the [4] _____ where relatives were buried provided the glue [5] _____ of keeping the family together. Younger family members, who seemed [6] _____, were urged to overcome their [7] _____ to "old-fashioned" customs. Too much "modern" life, they were told, [8] _____ away the fabric that held families together.

Exercise B *Answer the questions with complete explanations.*

1. Is your <u>ancestral</u> home the same as your <u>birthplace</u>?
   _____

2. When might keeping a prisoner <u>handcuffed</u> be a form of <u>brutality</u>?
   _____

3. How might <u>municipal</u> leaders <u>acknowledge</u> brave firefighters?
   _____

4. Why is the <u>abandonment</u> of life's <u>realities</u> dangerous?
   _____

Name _____ Date _____

"Choice: A Tribute to Dr. Martin Luther King, Jr." by Alice Walker
Reading Warm-up A

Read the following passage. Pay special attention to the underlined words. Then, read it again, and complete the activities. Use a separate sheet of paper for your written answers.

"Why can't we go to Orlando?" Keisha asked her parents. "That's my idea of a real vacation."

"Because, Keisha, dear," her mother answered, "we think it's time we introduced you to your heritage. We want you to spend some time in Georgia. Our people lived there for two hundred years. I cannot overstate the importance of experiencing that land and culture."

"But we've seen the family Bible that Daddy inherited from his father," Miles said. He had his own resistance to going along with his parents' plan. "What's the difference if we actually go to the cemetery where all those folks are buried? We can't see them anyhow."

"Your father and I think you're both capable of getting a lot out of visiting the old homestead, and Cousin Maggie is sure looking forward to our visit."

"If it's so great down there," Keisha said, "why did you ever leave?"

"In those days, there wasn't much opportunity for black people in that part of Georgia. Your grandparents thought my brothers and I would have a better chance of getting an education up north. People like your granddaddy were fearless in trying to change things, but my mamma was afraid it would take too long for us to be able to benefit from any changes. She said she wanted us to move before our brains rotted away."

Keisha smiled. "Oh, I guess it will be all right. Are you sure Cousin Maggie still has that old tire swing and that the pond hasn't dried up?"

Her mother laughed. Then, she said quietly, "You know, your daddy and I were thinking that if we all like it enough, maybe we'll move down there. I understand there's a brand-new community college that's looking for a few good teachers. It would be a great way to build a future—by reconnecting with the past."

1. Circle two words in the paragraph that help explain Keisha and Miles's heritage. Tell about two parts of your *heritage*.

2. Underline the two words that help to understand the meaning of importance. What is of great *importance* to you?

3. Underline the phrase that suggests the meaning of inherited. Describe something someone you know has *inherited*.

4. Circle the words that suggest the opposite of resistance. Write about something to which you have *resistance*.

5. Underline the words that define cemetery. Use two synonyms for *cemetery* in a sentence.

6. Circle the smaller word in capable that tells its meaning. What two things are you *capable* of?

7. Underline the antonym of fearless. Describe something about which you are *fearless*.

8. Rewrite the sentence with rotted, using a different word.

"Choice: A Tribute to Dr. Martin Luther King, Jr." by Alice Walker
Reading Warm-up B

Read the following passage. Pay special attention to the underlined words. Then, read it again, and complete the activities. Use a separate sheet of paper for your written answers.

As late as the 1960s, state laws in the South and underline{municipal} laws in southern cities allowed segregation, or separation, of blacks and whites. Unfair treatment of blacks was common. Black people were like outcasts in their own underline{birthplace}. Although a hundred years had passed since slavery ended, blacks were not truly free.

Many African Americans moved north. Blacks who did not favor underline{abandonment} of their underline{ancestral} homeland had two choices. They could continue to live without equality or they could try to end segregation.

Dr. Martin Luther King, Jr., a minister from Atlanta, became a leader of the civil rights movement by preaching nonviolence. His weapons were not guns and clubs but boycotts, sit-ins, and demonstrations and marches.

The most famous boycott, or refusal to do something, addressed one of the everyday underline{realities} of black people's lives. They had to sit at the backs of buses and give up their seats to white people. One day in 1955, in Montgomery, Alabama, a woman named Rosa Parks refused. Then, other African Americans refused to take the bus. This nonviolent boycott lasted a whole year. In 1956, the U.S. Supreme Court ruled that such unfair treatment of blacks was unconstitutional.

The sit-in movement began in 1960, in Greensboro, North Carolina. There, African American students protested segregation at lunch counters. They "sat in" and refused to leave. As the movement spread, Dr. King urged protesters not to respond to police underline{brutality} with their own violence. Though they might be underline{handcuffed}, beaten, or arrested, they were not to fight back physically.

Demonstrations were aimed at ending school segregation and registering African Americans to vote. The police and even white citizens often used violence to try to stop the civil rights movement, but in the end, they had to underline{acknowledge} that the demonstrators were winning. National laws were passed to make unfair treatment illegal. It was now up to people to obey the laws.

1. Circle the word that helps you understand what underline{municipal} laws are. Tell about a *municipal* service where you live.

2. Circle the two words that make up underline{birthplace}. Write a sentence about your *birthplace*.

3. Underline the phrase in the next sentence that is the opposite of underline{abandonment}. Describe the effects of *abandonment* on a house.

4. Circle the word that suggests the meaning of underline{ancestral}. Use *ancestral* in a sentence of your own.

5. Circle the root word of underline{realities}. Tell about three *realities* of your life.

6. Underline a synonym for underline{brutality}. Describe an act of *brutality*.

7. Circle the word that tells who might be underline{handcuffed}. Name two things a *handcuffed* person cannot do.

8. Circle the words that tell what people had to underline{acknowledge}. What do you *acknowledge* to be true?

"Choice: A Tribute to Dr. Martin Luther King, Jr." by Alice Walker
Reading: Set a Purpose for Reading and Adjust Your Reading Rate

When you **set a purpose for reading,** you determine your focus before reading a written work. Once you have set a purpose, **adjust your reading rate** according to that goal. When you read to learn new information, read slowly and carefully. Take time to think about what you have read. Reread, if necessary, to clarify your understanding. When you read for entertainment, you may read more quickly.

DIRECTIONS: *Answer the questions below about setting a purpose and adjusting your reading rate.*

1. What purpose might you set for reading a speech by Dr. Martin Luther King, Jr.?
_____

2. What reading rate might you set for reading this speech? _____

3. What purpose might you set for reading a collection of short stories by Alice Walker? _____

4. What reading rate might you set for reading the stories? _____

5. What purpose might you set for reading a magazine article about Dr. King in a popular magazine? _____

6. What reading rate might you set for reading the article? _____

7. What purpose might you set for reading a detailed review of Alice Walker's novels?
_____

8. What reading rate might you set for reading the detailed review? _____
_____

"Choice: A Tribute to Dr. Martin Luther King, Jr." by Alice Walker
Literary Analysis: Author's Influences

An **author's influences** are the cultural and historical factors that affect his or her writing. These factors include the time and place of an author's birth and life, the author's cultural background, or world events that happened during the author's lifetime. Read biographical information to learn about an author's influences. When reading an author's work, look for references to details that show cultural or historical attitudes. Consider these passages from "Choice: A Tribute to Dr. Martin Luther King, Jr."

> My great-great-great-grandmother walked as a slave from Virginia to Eatonton, Georgia— which passes for the Walker ancestral home—with two babies on her hips.

> In 1960, my mother bought a television set, and each day after school I watched Hamilton Holmes and Charlayne Hunter as they struggled to integrate—fair-skinned as they were— the University of Georgia.

The first passage tells you that the writer, Alice Walker, is an African American woman descended from slaves. The second passage tells you that during her school years, she watched other African American students struggle for the right to enter college. These passages locate Alice Walker in time (during the 1960s) and place (the South) and suggest that the selection reflects on the civil rights movement.

DIRECTIONS: *Read the passage below from "Choice: A Tribute to Martin Luther King, Jr.," and answer the questions.*

> At the moment I first saw [Dr. Martin Luther King, Jr.] he was being handcuffed and shoved into a police truck. He had dared to claim his rights as a native son, and had been arrested. He displayed no fear, but seemed calm and serene, unaware of his own extraordinary courage. . . . At the moment I saw his resistance I knew I would never be able to live in this country without resisting everything that sought to disinherit me . . .

1. Who inspired Alice Walker to resist the racism against African American people in America? _____

2. What impressed Walker about Dr. King?

   _____

3. How did America see Alice Walker and other African Americans in this historical period, according to the author's words in the passage?

   _____

   _____

"Choice: A Tribute to Dr. Martin Luther King, Jr." by Alice Walker
Vocabulary Builder

Word List

| sensibility | revolutionary | disinherited |

A. DIRECTIONS: *For each item below, think about the meaning of the italicized Word List word, and then answer the question.*

1. If your aunt has an artistic *sensibility,* how would she feel about going to plays?

   _____

2. Did Dr. King make *revolutionary* changes in America's social structure? Explain.

   _____

3. If a group has been *disinherited,* how have its rights been changed?

   _____

B. DIRECTIONS: *For each item, decide which choice means the* **opposite** *of the numbered word.*

1. sensibility
   A. insensitivity
   B. knowledge
   C. dislike
   D. hatred
2. revolutionary
   A. clean
   B. new
   C. ordinary
   D. historical
3. disinherited
   A. fought
   B. chosen
   C. worked
   D. given

"Choice: A Tribute to Dr. Martin Luther King, Jr." by Alice Walker
Support for Writing a Speech

To prepare to write a **speech** for the dedication of a local monument to Dr. Martin Luther King, Jr., enter important information into the chart below.

Dr. King and His Legacy	
Why Dr. King's ideas are important in today's world	_____ _____ _____ _____ _____ _____
Why Dr. King should be remembered	_____ _____ _____ _____ _____ _____
Vivid words and phrases	_____ _____ _____ _____ _____ _____
Words and phrases to be repeated	_____ _____ _____ _____ _____ _____

On a separate page, write a draft of your speech for the dedication of a monument. Use material from both Dr. King and Alice Walker to support why the monument is deserved.

"Choice: A Tribute to Dr. Martin Luther King, Jr." by Alice Walker
Support for Extend Your Learning

Research and Technology

As you gather information for your **newspaper article** for Dr. King Day, fill in the chart below.

Dr. King's Birthday: A Celebration	
Important information on Dr. King's life	
Dramatic sentence for lead to newspaper article	
Quotes from King, Walker, others	

Listening and Speaking

As you prepare with a classmate to **role-play** an interview with a civil rights marcher from the era of Dr. Martin Luther King, Jr., do the following:

- Decide which of you will be the interviewer and which will be the interviewee.
- Read firsthand accounts of a historic march, such as the 1965 march from Selma to Montgomery, Alabama.
- Practice your roles as questioner and interviewee.
- Present your role play to your class.

"Choice: A Tribute to Dr. Martin Luther King, Jr." by Alice Walker
Enrichment: The Words of Dr. Martin Luther King, Jr.

In "Choice: A Tribute to Dr. Martin Luther King, Jr.," Alice Walker writes about several ways in which Dr. King affected people. The list includes:

A. He had courage.

B. He had a revolutionary personal and social philosophy.

C. He challenged the United States to solve its racial problems.

D. He addressed the problems of southern African Americans.

DIRECTIONS: *Read each passage from one of Dr. King's speeches below. Choose the letter above that best goes with each passage, and write it in the blank.*

1. From "I Have a Dream"—March on Washington, August 28, 1963

   _____ " . . . So let freedom ring from the prodigious hilltops of New Hampshire. . . . let freedom ring from Stone Mountain of Georgia! Let freedom ring from Lookout Mountain of Tennessee! . . . From every mountainside, let freedom ring."

2. From "I Have a Dream"—March on Washington, August 28, 1963

   _____ " . . . I have a dream that my four children will one day live in a nation where they will not be judged by the color of their skin but by the content of their character. I have a dream today."

3. From "Beyond Vietnam"—Riverside Church, New York, April 4, 1967

   _____ "A few years ago there was a shining moment. . . . It seemed as if there was a real promise of hope for the poor, both black and white, through the poverty program. . . . Then came the buildup in Vietnam, and I watched this program [become] broken. . . . And I know that America would never invest the necessary funds or energies in rehabilitation of its poor so long as adventures like Vietnam continued . . . "

4. From "I've Been to the Mountaintop,"—Memphis, Tennessee, April 3, 1968

   _____ " . . . I've been to the mountaintop. . . . And I've seen the promised land. I may not get there with you. But I want you to know tonight, that we, as a people, will get to the promised land. . . . I'm not fearing any man. . . . "

"Choice: A Tribute to Dr. Martin Luther King, Jr." by Alice Walker
Selection Test A

Critical Reading *Identify the letter of the choice that best answers the question.*

____ 1. What reading rate would be best to use as you read "Choice: A Tribute to Dr. Martin Luther King, Jr."?

    A. slow, to get all the details

    B. skim, to get the main ideas

    C. normal speed, to be entertained

    D. slightly faster than normal speed

____ 2. "Choice: A Tribute to Dr. Martin Luther King, Jr.," begins with the lines, "My great-great-great-grandmother walked as a slave from to Virginia to Eatonton, Georgia—which passes for the Walker ancestral home—with two babies on her hips." What do these lines tell you about Alice Walker's influences?

    A. She had a large, extended southern family.

    B. She is a fifth generation writer.

    C. She was born in the 1940s.

    D. She is an African American descended from slaves.

____ 3. Walker discusses her family history in the opening paragraphs of "Choice: A Tribute to Dr. Martin Luther King, Jr." What is the historical background of her discussion?

    A. the American civil rights movement

    B. slavery and its aftermath

    C. modern-day Georgia

    D. the Revolutionary War

____ 4. Which of the following questions would help you set a purpose for reading "Choice: A Tribute to Dr. Martin Luther King, Jr."?

    A. Why did some families have only one television?

    B. Why do families live in the same place for many years?

    C. Why did African Americans leave the South?

    D. What information can I find about Dr. King on the internet?

Name _____ Date _____

_____ 5. Historical factors influence authors and their writing. Which historical factors that affected Alice Walker are shown in this passage?

> Yet the history of my family, like that of all black Southerners, is a history of dispossession. We loved the land and we worked the land, but we never owned it.

A. African Americans had a history of successful farming.

B. African Americans, despite long histories, could not claim land or a heritage.

C. Because of long family histories, African Americans often inherited land.

D. Possessions are what African American people wanted most.

_____ 6. According to Walker, if an African American chose to stay in the South before the 1960s, what would be the reason?

A. The person was strong and stubborn.

B. The person was attached to memories.

C. The person was afraid to fly.

D. The person owned land.

_____ 7. When Walker sees Dr. King on television, she is impressed with his calm courage. What purpose would you set for continuing to read the selection after this?

A. to be persuaded to join a modern-day civil rights movement

B. to learn about technological advances in television

C. to learn what impact Dr. King's life would have on the author

D. to do research on the kind of news stories television covers

_____ 8. In "Choice: A Tribute to Dr. Martin Luther King, Jr.," what is the most important thing Dr. King gives to Alice Walker?

A. a personally signed copy of his book

B. the joy of listening to him preach

C. the courage to work for change

D. the motivation to become a writer

_____ 9. How does Walker say that Dr. King gave African Americans back their heritage?

A. He encouraged those who left the South to come home to fight for their rights.

B. He obtained the rights to the land stolen from them following Reconstruction.

C. He preached and brought them back into the church in which they grew up.

D. He fought for rights that would allow them to live more freely in the South, and enjoy a sense of home.

_____ 10. According to "Choice: A Tribute to Dr. Martin Luther King, Jr.," which best describes Dr. King's philosophy?

    A. peaceful and meditative

    B. materialistic and realistic

    C. complex and revolutionary

    D. forceful and violent

Vocabulary and Grammar

_____ 11. In which sentence is the meaning of the word *revolutionary* expressed?

    A. African American southerners often left the South after Reconstruction.

    B. Dr. King's philosophy changed the way of life in the South.

    C. Many African American southerners prayed regularly for Dr. King's safety.

    D. Dr. King's speeches can be heard virtually anywhere today.

_____ 12. Which of the following is correctly capitalized?

    A. dr. martin luther king, jr.

    B. Dr. Martin Luther King, Jr.

    C. dr. Martin Luther King, Jr.

    D. Dr. Martin Luther King, jr.

Essay

13. Think about your reading of "Choice: A Tribute to Dr. Martin Luther King, Jr." Do you think the age at which Alice Walker was exposed to the actions of Dr. King played a part in the importance he has had in her life? Write a brief essay stating whether you think her age did or did not play a major role, and give your reasons.

14. Which of the characteristics of Dr. King's life and work, as revealed in Alice Walker's speech "Choice: A Tribute to Dr. Martin Luther King, Jr.," do you find the most important or worthy of admiration? Write a brief essay stating your opinion and giving your reasons.

"Choice: A Tribute to Dr. Martin Luther King, Jr." by Alice Walker
Selection Test B

Critical Reading *Identify the letter of the choice that best completes the statement or answers the question.*

_____ 1. Which of these would you probably read slowly, followed by rereading passages?
  A. a magazine article about the making of the film *The Color Purple*
  B. the novel or script of *The Color Purple*
  C. critical essays that discuss Alice Walker's writing in detail
  D. a newspaper feature about the town in which Alice Walker grew up

_____ 2. After reading this passage from "Choice: A Tribute to Dr. Martin Luther King, Jr.," what purpose would you set for continuing to read the selection?

  I watched my brothers, one by one, leave our home and leave the South. I watched my sisters do the same.

  A. to read the letters they wrote home
  B. to learn why they left the South
  C. to be persuaded to live in the North
  D. to be entertained by their travel stories

_____ 3. What is the historical background of Walker's discussion of her family history?
  A. the American civil rights movement
  B. African enslavement and its aftermath
  C. modern-day Georgia
  D. Revolutionary War

_____ 4. What is the meaning of this passage from "Choice: A Tribute to Dr. Martin Luther King, Jr."?

  If it is true that land does not belong to anyone until they have buried a body in it, then the land of my birthplace belongs to me, dozens of times over.

  A. Walker claims spiritual ownership of land where her kin are buried.
  B. Walker has helped bury dozens of relatives in her own yard.
  C. Only people who have owned land can be buried on it when they die.
  D. Walker has bought the property on which her relatives are buried.

_____ 5. What major cultural and historical factor is reflected in the middle portion of "Choice: A Tribute to Dr. Martin Luther King, Jr."?
  A. the American civil rights movement
  B. Walker's ancestors' lives
  C. slavery during the Civil War
  D. African Americans' lives today

_____ 6. Why can you conclude from "Choice: A Tribute to Dr. Martin Luther King, Jr." that the Walkers feared Dr. King would be murdered?
  A. They knew he had a lot of courage.
  B. The guarded him when he spoke.
  C. They prayed for his safety.
  D. They saw his sense of peace.

____ 7. What purpose would you set for continuing to read "Choice: A Tribute to Dr. Martin Luther King, Jr." after reading this passage?

> And then, one day, there appeared the face of Dr. Martin Luther King, Jr. What a funny name, I thought. At the moment I first saw him, he was being handcuffed and shoved into a police truck.

    A. to learn more about Dr. King's work
    B. to become a news photographer
    C. to do research on police procedures
    D. to read more jokes about funny names

____ 8. In "Choice: A Tribute to Dr. Martin Luther King, Jr.," what does the author mean by *disinherit* when she says that she would resist everything that sought to disinherit her?

    A. She would resist efforts to keep her from inheriting family land.
    B. She would resist efforts to keep her out of her father's will.
    C. She would resist efforts to keep her from buying back her property.
    D. She would resist efforts to keep her from gaining her civil rights.

____ 9. According to "Choice: A Tribute to Dr. Martin Luther King, Jr.," what does the author think of King's philosophy?

    I. It was revealed to very few people.
    II. Few people are capable of understanding it fully.
    III. It is revolutionary.
    IV. Few people have the patience to live it.
    A. I, II, III
    B. I, II, IV
    C. II, III, IV
    D. I, III, IV

____ 10. Besides African Americans, whom else did Dr. King believe to be disinherited, according to "Choice: A Tribute to Dr. Martin Luther King, Jr."?

    I. poor whites
    II. American Indians
    III. politicians
    IV. Mexican Americans
    A. I, II, III
    B. II, III, IV
    C. I, II, IV
    D. I, III, IV

____ 11. What is symbolic about the location Walker chooses for her speech?
    A. It is given in Dr. King's hometown.
    B. It is given in a restaurant that would not have admitted African Americans before King.
    C. It is given in the Walker hometown.
    D. It is given to librarians who will not allow the works of Dr. King in their libraries.

____ 12. What is the "Choice" in the title "Choice: A Tribute to Dr. Martin Luther King, Jr."?
   A. to be friends with whomever you choose
   B. to leave your place of birth in the South to go to the North
   C. to say what you choose without fear of others' criticism
   D. to live where you choose and not face racial prejudice

Vocabulary and Grammar

____ 13. In which sentence is the meaning of the word *disinherited* expressed?
   A. It is impossible to tell where Walker's relative is buried.
   B. African Americans were not allowed to own the land they lived on.
   C. Dr. King seemed unaware of his extraordinary courage and strength.
   D. It was not unusual for southern African Americans to move north.

____ 14. In which sentence is the meaning of the word *revolutionary* expressed?
   A. Dr. King's courage was inspiring to others in the struggle.
   B. Dr. King tended to think little of prizes or awards.
   C. Dr. King gave southern African Americans back their heritage.
   D. Dr. King's philosophy led to sweeping changes in society.

____ 15. Which of the following is correctly capitalized?
   A. Civil War and Reconstruction period
   B. civil war and reconstruction period
   C. Civil War and reconstruction period
   D. Civil war and reconstruction period

____ 16. Which of the following is correctly capitalized?
   A. the American Indian, the Mexican American, and the Poor American White
   B. the American indian, the mexican American, and the poor American white
   C. the American Indian, the Mexican American, and the poor American white
   D. the american Indian, the Mexican american, and the poor american white

Essay

17. According to Alice Walker in "Choice: A Tribute to Dr. Martin Luther King, Jr.," what was King's most important gift to African Americans? Write a brief essay to state your opinion. Give at least two examples from the speech to support it.

18. What purpose did you set for reading "Choice: A Tribute to Dr. Martin Luther King, Jr."? How fast or slowly did you read it? Write a brief essay that explains your choices.

19. What does Alice Walker mean in "Choice: A Tribute to Dr. Martin Luther King, Jr." when she says, "The public acts of Dr. King you know. They are visible all around you." Write a brief essay explaining what you think she means. Give examples from the text and from your own historical knowledge.

Vocabulary Warm-up Word Lists

Study these words from the "An Episode of War." Then, complete the activities.

Word List A

ambulances [AM byuh luhns uhz] *n.* hospital vehicles
  <u>Ambulances</u> took the injured workers to the hospital.

assault [uh SAWLT] *n.* an attack, often by an army
  During the <u>assault</u> on our fort, we were pelted with snowballs.

assistance [uh SIS tuhns] *n.* help
  I would welcome your <u>assistance</u> to move the dresser.

corps [KAWR] *n.* military group trained for special duties
  The hospital <u>corps</u> was close to the battlefield.

encouragement [en KER ij muhnt] *n.* support that helps someone
  My parents give me a lot of <u>encouragement</u> to succeed in school.

engaged [en GAYJD] *v.* took part in
  I <u>engaged</u> in a tug-of-war with my brother for the remote control.

menace [MEN is] *n.* someone or something that is dangerous
  The club on the corner is a <u>menace</u> to our peace and quiet.

representatives [rep ri ZEN tuh tivz] *n.* people acting for others
  <u>Representatives</u> of the committee met to discuss school issues.

Word List B

headlong [HED lawng] *adv.* moving quickly, head first
  The runner dove <u>headlong</u> across the goal line.

lieutenant [loo TEN uhnt] *n.* a military officer of low rank
  The captain gave orders to the <u>lieutenant</u>, who passed them along.

scabbard [SKA buhrd] *n.* a sheath, or holder, for a sword
  An ancient Japanese sword hangs in a <u>scabbard</u> on the wall.

spectators [SPEK tay terz] *n.* people who watch something
  <u>Spectators</u> at the stadium cheered the back-to-back home runs.

squad [SKWAHD] *n.* a group of people doing the same activity
  A <u>squad</u> of soldiers went to scout out the nearby area.

stragglers [STRAG lerz] *n.* those who lag behind
  When the show began, there were still <u>stragglers</u> in the lobby.

sympathetically [sim puh THET ik lee] *adv.* with feelings
  We greeted the firefighter's widow <u>sympathetically</u>.

"An Episode of War" by Stephen Crane
Vocabulary Warm-up Exercises

Exercise A *Fill in each blank in the paragraph below with an appropriate word from Word List A. Use each word only once.*

In the [1] _____ on our stronghold, many of our soldiers received bullet holes in their skin or other flesh wounds. Emergency teams, arriving in [2] _____, managed to get the worst hit soldiers off the hill and on toward the hospital in town. With the able [3] _____ of caring medical staff, we hoped they would all recover. As the wounded were lifted or walked into the vans, we gave them as much [4] _____ as we could. I even managed a smile. Then, [5] _____ of our military [6] _____ gathered the rest of us together. They [7] _____ us in some quick strategy planning, for we knew the [8] _____, or present danger, was far from over. With skill and luck, we would have the strength to hold off another attack.

Exercise B *Answer the questions with complete explanations.*

1. Would a guitar player keep his instrument in a <u>scabbard</u>?

   _____

2. Might a <u>lieutenant</u> yell at the soldiers under his command <u>sympathetically</u>?

   _____

3. Do <u>spectators</u> at the Olympics take part in the games?

   _____

4. Is it a good idea to go downstairs <u>headlong</u>?

   _____

5. If you were among the <u>stragglers</u>, would you be the first to get back to your bus?

   _____

6. If you liked to do things all alone, would you enjoy being part of a <u>squad</u>?

   _____

Name _____ Date _____

"An Episode of War" by Stephen Crane
Reading Warm-up A

Read the following passage. Pay special attention to the underlined words. Then, read it again, and complete the activities. Use a separate sheet of paper for your written answers.

In the mid-1800s, how did the leaders of the divided northern and southern states put together armies to fight the Civil War?

The Civil War was the first war for which the American government tried to draft men into the army. Actually, the threat of being forced to join was enough to make many men enlist, or sign up. Fewer than 50,000 men had to be forced to give <u>assistance</u> to their country. To get Americans to sign up, some had to be given <u>encouragement</u> in the form of cash awards.

The northern and southern armies were each made up of <u>representatives</u> of all states and all walks of life. There were many ways to support the war effort besides taking part in an <u>assault</u> on the enemy. Workers were needed to load and unload supplies. Strong men were needed to operate the <u>ambulances</u>, wagons used to remove the sick and injured from the battlefield. In field hospitals, doctors and nurses tended these soldiers.

At first, soldiers' spirits ran high. The North was fighting to protect the country from the <u>menace</u> of southern states seceding, or withdrawing, from the Union. Meanwhile, the South was fighting for that very right.

The war dragged on. As thousands of soldiers died, morale dropped. Younger and younger men—boys, actually —were needed. Some <u>engaged</u> in draft dodging, or avoiding being taken into the army. Rich families could do so legally. A man with money could simply pay someone to take his place. A business even grew up to find substitute soldiers for those who could not find them on their own.

Sometimes, a soldier found the war too painful. Then, he deserted, or illegally left, his <u>corps</u>. In some cases, soldiers got out of service legally because of personal or physical problems. Thousands of soldiers, however, plodded through the war, despite everything. They were probably the true heroes. Fortunately, some lived to tell their horrible wartime experiences.

1. Circle the words that tell what some men were forced to give <u>assistance</u> to. Describe a time when you gave *assistance*.

2. Circle the words that tell what was used for <u>encouragement</u>. What kind of *encouragement* helps you do something?

3. Circle the words that describe the army's <u>representatives</u>. Describe something you know that has *representatives*.

4. Underline the word that helps you understand <u>assault</u>. Describe an *assault* in war today.

5. Underline what <u>ambulances</u> were during the Civil War. Describe modern *ambulances*.

6. Circle the words that identify the <u>menace</u>. Name a *menace* today.

7. Circle what some soldiers <u>engaged</u> in. Rewrite the sentence, replacing *engaged* with a word or phrase.

8. Circle the word in the following sentence that helps to understand <u>corps</u>. Explain what *corps* means.

"An Episode of War" by Stephen Crane
Reading Warm-up B

Read the following passage. Pay special attention to the underlined words. Then, read it again, and complete the activities. Use a separate sheet of paper for your written answers.

Although the Civil War was bloody, disease—not bullets—was the war's great killer. At least two-thirds of all deaths were due to illness and doctors' failure to treat it.

The problem was that doctors knew little about the causes and cures of sickness back then. They did not even know that germs caused disease!

Doctors became <u>spectators</u> of the terrible march of disease through the ranks. From a company's foot soldiers to its <u>lieutenant</u> to its general, no one was safe. A whole <u>squad</u> of soldiers might be lost in a few days from an illness that a simple modern treatment could cure today.

Of course, the ways of war did not help. An officer on horseback, sword pulled from <u>scabbard</u>, made a dashing sight. Yet, he was an easy target for the enemy. When soldiers on foot ran <u>headlong</u> into battle, guns and cannons easily knocked them down. Their chances of survival probably were not much better if they got to a hospital sooner rather than later.

Many times, one soldier recovering from a bullet wound would lie next to one suffering from a dangerous disease. The illness would spread easily, and no one would know how to stop it. When soldiers were taken from field hospitals to general hospitals far from the battlefield, again the ill and the injured lay side by side. Probably, the best thing for patients was to get out of the hospital quickly because the <u>stragglers</u> would usually just get sicker.

The situation was worse in the South than in the North. The North had placed an embargo, or ban, on medicine, medical supplies, and even medical books to the South. The South had to make its own medicine and use local plants that were known to have healing powers.

One of the few positive things to come from the treatment of the sick and injured was the growth of nursing. Women tended <u>sympathetically</u> to the slightly injured and the most hopeless cases alike. They made the unbearable just a little bearable.

1. Circle the word that identifies who became <u>spectators</u>. Tell about a time you and your friends were *spectators*.

2. Explain who are lower in rank than the <u>lieutenant</u>, and higher.

3. Underline the word that helps explain <u>squad</u>. Write a sentence using *squad*.

4. Underline the words that help you figure out the meaning of <u>scabbard</u>. Explain why a *scabbard* was important.

5. Circle the word that tells who ran <u>headlong</u>. Describe an activity in which you could move *headlong*.

6. Underline the word that, by contrast, hints at the meaning of <u>stragglers</u>. What situation might be dangerous for *stragglers*?

7. Circle the sentence that tells the result of acting <u>sympathetically</u>. Describe a time that someone you know acted *sympathetically*.

"An Episode of War" by Stephen Crane

Reading: Set a Purpose for Reading and Adjust Your Reading Rate

When you **set a purpose for reading,** you determine your focus before reading a written work. Once you have set a purpose, **adjust your reading rate** according to that goal. You might read fiction for both entertainment and information. Entertainment does not always mean amusement or enjoyment. It can also mean that you learn about characters and why they act as they do. When you read fiction that is written more formally than today's writing, read slowly and carefully. Reread long sentences, or material with unfamiliar facts and content. When you read modern fiction, you can usually read faster. Nonfiction, both older and modern, needs careful reading and rereading so that you can understand important information.

DIRECTIONS: *Answer the questions about setting purpose and adjusting reading rate.*

1. What purpose might you set for reading Stephen Crane's famous novel of the Civil War, *The Red Badge of Courage,* published in 1895?

   _____

2. What reading rate might you set for reading this novel?

   _____

3. What purpose might you set for reading nonfiction accounts of Civil War battles?

   _____

4. What reading rate might you set for reading about Civil War battles?

   _____

5. What purpose might you set for reading a short story about the Vietnam War?

   _____

6. What reading rate might you use for reading this story?

   _____

7. What purpose might you set for reading a modern novel about war?

   _____

8. What reading rate might you use for reading a modern novel about war?

   _____

"An Episode of War" by Stephen Crane
Literary Analysis: Author's Influences

An **author's influences** are the cultural and historical factors that affect his or her writing. These factors may include the time and place of an author's birth and life, the author's cultural background, or world events that happened during the author's lifetime. Read the following facts about the Civil War and Stephen Crane.

A. Civil War field hospitals were unclean and crowded with wounded soldiers.

B. Medical practices included cutting off injured limbs to keep soldiers from dying from infection.

C. Crane was fascinated by war. He interviewed Civil War veterans, and studied battlefield maps and accounts of the fighting.

DIRECTIONS: *Read each passage from "An Episode of War." Decide which of the historical and cultural factors above is reflected in the passage. Write the correct letter or letters in the blank.*

1. _____ As the wounded officer passed from the line of battle, he was enabled to see many things which as a participant in the fight were unknown to him.

2. _____ An interminable [unending] crowd of bandaged men were coming and going. Great numbers sat under the trees nursing heads or arms or legs.

3. _____ "Nonsense, man! Nonsense! Nonsense!" cried the doctor. "Come along, now. I won't amputate it. Come along. Don't be a baby."

   "Let go of me," said the lieutenant, holding back wrathfully, his glance fixed upon the door of the old schoolhouse, as sinister to him as the portals of death.

4. _____ A battery, a tumultuous and shining mass, was swirling toward the right. The wild thud of hoofs, the cries of the riders shouting blame and praise, menace and encouragement, and last, the roar of the wheels, the slant of the glistening guns, brought the lieutenant to an intent pause.

"An Episode of War" by Stephen Crane
Vocabulary Builder

Word List

| compelled   tumultuous   contempt |

A. DIRECTIONS: *For each item below, think about the meaning of the italicized Word List word, and then answer the question.*

1. How would you feel if a friend *compelled* you to go to party you didn't want to go to?

   _____

2. How would someone in the grip of *tumultuous* emotions handle a surprise event? Explain.

   _____

3. What kind of behavior would cause you to have *contempt* for a person?

   _____

B. DIRECTIONS: *For each item below, decide which choice means the same or about the same as the numbered word.*

1. compelled
   - A. freed
   - B. ordered
   - C. released
   - D. angered
2. tumultuous
   - A. calm
   - B. refreshed
   - C. upset
   - D. annoyed
3. contempt
   - A. respect
   - B. puzzlement
   - C. admiration
   - D. scorn

"An Episode of War" by Stephen Crane
Support for Writing a Speech

To prepare to write a **speech** for the dedication of a local monument to the soldiers of the Civil War, enter important information into the chart below.

The Common Soldier: Courage and Determination	
Details from "An Episode of War" about hardships of war on soldiers	
Why Civil War soldiers deserve to be remembered and honored	
Vivid words and phrases	

On a separate page, write a draft for your speech. Remember to include words and phrases that can be repeated for a strong impact. In addition, leave spaces for dramatic pauses that can make your listeners pay extra attention.

"An Episode of War" by Stephen Crane
Support for Extend Your Learning

Research and Technology

As you gather information for your **newspaper article** about the cost and experience of fighting in the Civil War, enter important information and statistics in the chart below.

The Cost of the War: Was It Worth It?	
Attention-grabbing lead for story	
Information about numbers: cost of war, number of dead and injured, and so on	
Quotes from "An Episode of War" about personal experiences of war	

Listening and Speaking

As you and a classmate prepare to **role-play** an interview with the lieutenant from "An Episode of War," do the following:

- Decide who will be the lieutenant and who will be the news reporter.
- Read firsthand accounts of a Civil War battle, such as Gettysburg.
- Present the role play to your classroom.

"An Episode of War" by Stephen Crane
Enrichment: Media Messages

You have learned that Stephen Crane's writing on war changed readers' views of wartime. His realism was different from writing that made war seem like an exciting adventure. Read the following passage from Crane's classic novel *The Red Badge of Courage*. Then, on the lines provided, write two short paragraphs that identify Crane's message about war and compare it to a war movie or video battle game you are familiar with.

From *The Red Badge of Courage*:

He came finally to a road from which he could see in the distance dark . . . bodies of troops, smoke-fringed. In the lane was a blood-stained crowd streaming to the rear. The wounded men were cursing, groaning, and wailing. . . .

One of the wounded men had a shoeful of blood. He hopped like a schoolboy in a game. He was laughing hysterically.

One was swearing that he had been shot in the arm through the commanding general's mismanagement of the army. One was marching with . . . an unholy mixture of merriment and agony. . . .

Another had the gray seal of death already upon his face. His lips were curled in hard lines and his teeth were clinched. His hands were bloody from where he had pressed them on his wound. He seemed to be waiting the moment when he should pitch headlong. . . his eyes burning with the power of a stare into the unknown.

_____

_____

_____

_____

_____

_____

_____

_____

_____

_____

_____

_____

_____

_____

"Choice: A Tribute to Dr. Martin Luther King, Jr." by Alice Walker
"An Episode of War" by Stephen Crane
Build Language Skills: Vocabulary

Borrowed and Foreign Words

Many English words have been taken from other languages. Many words that name foods have been borrowed. The word *coleslaw* comes from the Dutch word *kool sla*, which means "cabbage salad."

A. DIRECTIONS: *Look at the list of words below, and the languages from which they were taken. Use each word to fill one of the blanks in the sentences.*

French: *chowder, salad*
Spanish: *chili con carne, salsa*
German: *frankfurter, sauerkraut*

1. As an appetizer, my sister ordered a basket of chips with _____ as a dip.
2. My grandfather ordered a _____ with _____, only he called it a hot dog and cabbage.
3. My father loves fish, so he ordered a big bowl of clam soup, or _____.
4. I ordered a big bowl of _____, because I love spicy dishes with meat and beans.
5. My aunt loves lettuce, so she ordered a _____.

Academic Vocabulary Practice

critique	skim	focus	identify	revise

B. DIRECTIONS: *Use one of the words from the box as a synonym to replace the italicized word in each sentence. Rewrite the sentence using one of the words in the box.*

1. The witness was unable to *recognize* the man she saw running from the fire.

   _____

2. Don't *speed* through the story or you'll miss the humor.

   _____

3. I'm trying to *concentrate* on my homework, so please turn down the radio.

   _____

4. We'll have to *adjust* our plans for the building.

   _____

5. Please prepare a *review* of the movie you saw last night.

   _____

Name _____ Date _____

Build Language Skills: Grammar

Capitalization

Use a capital letter at the beginning of a sentence. Also, use a capital for the first letter of a proper noun or proper adjective.

Stephen **C**rane is a well-known **A**merican short-story writer.

A. DIRECTIONS: *Rewrite each sentence below. Substitute capital letters or lowercase letters where they belong.*

1. Alice walker's life was deeply affected by dr. martin luther king, jr., the civil rights Leader.

   _____

2. she loved to hear him preach at ebenezer baptist church.

   _____

3. alice was changed when she watched two African American Students try to Enroll at the university of georgia.

   _____

4. she says that many black Americans feel more comfortable in the south because of Dr. king's Life.

   _____

B. DIRECTIONS: *Write a short paragraph about a person, place, or event that has affected you. Be sure to capitalize the first word of each sentence as well as proper nouns and proper adjectives.*

_____

_____

_____

_____

_____

_____

_____

_____

_____

"An Episode of War" by Stephen Crane
Selection Test A

Critical Reading *Identify the letter of the choice that best answers the question.*

____ 1. What purpose would you set for reading further after reading this passage from "An Episode of War"?

> . . . when suddenly the lieutenant cried out and looked quickly at a man near him as if he suspected it was a case of personal assault. The others cried out also when they saw blood upon the lieutenant's sleeve.

A. to learn whether the lieutenant is brave or cowardly

B. to learn what made the blood on the lieutenant's sleeve

C. to find out who the man near the lieutenant is

D. to learn what kinds of wounds afflict people in war

____ 2. Which reasons would make you set a slow reading rate for the following passage from "An Episode of War"?

> His lips pursed as he drew with his sword various crevices in the heap, until brown squares of coffee, astoundingly equal in size, appeared on the blanket.

I. long sentence

II. difficult vocabulary

III. wartime setting

IV. several phrases

A. I, II, III

B. I, III, and IV

C. II, III, and IV

D. I, II, and IV

____ 3. What purpose would you most likely set for reading "An Episode of War"?

A. to learn how to fight with a sword

B. to understand more about camp cooking

C. to learn about the Civil War

D. to understand how messages were delivered

____ 4. What can you conclude about what has happened when the lieutenant is injured?

A. He has been injured by the man near him.

B. He has been shot by an enemy sitting in a tree.

C. He has been injured by a sword slash.

D. He has been shot by a stray bullet.

____ 5. Stephen Crane's fascination with the Civil War was one of the influences on his life and writing. Read this passage from "An Episode of War." Which of the following facts contributed to Crane's writing of this passage?

> A wound gives strange dignity to him to bears it. Well men shy from his new and terrible majesty.

    A. Crane was born well after the Civil War had ended.

    B. Army field hospitals were unsanitary and badly supplied.

    C. Civil War vets told Crane what it was like to be wounded.

    D. Many wounded men lost their limbs due to infection.

____ 6. In "An Episode of War," how do the lieutenant's comrades react to his being shot?

    I.   They are sympathetic.

    II. They are unconcerned.

    III. They are afraid to touch him.

    IV. They plan revenge on the enemy.

    A. I, II

    B. II, III

    C. III, IV

    D. I, III

____ 7. Stephen Crane's fascination with the Civil War was one of the influences on his life and writing. Read this passage. Which of the following facts contributed to Crane's writing of this passage?

> An aide galloped furiously, dragged his horse suddenly to a halt, saluted, and presented a paper. It was, for a wonder, precisely like a historical painting.

    A. Crane examined photographs of the battle sites.

    B. Crane was a reporter before he wrote fiction.

    C. Civil War hospitals were crowded with soldiers.

    D. Crane was fascinated by the Civil War.

____ 8. What can you conclude about soldiers' feelings in wartime from this passage?

> He [an officer] bound his handkerchief over the wound, scolding away in the meantime. . . . The lieutenant hung his head, feeling, in this presence, that he did not know how to be correctly wounded.

    A. Soldiers were enraged when they were wounded.

    B. Soldiers were frightened when they were wounded.

    C. Soldiers were unworried when they were wounded.

    D. Soldiers were ashamed when they were wounded.

___ 9. In "An Episode of War," how do the medical people at the field hospital treat the lieutenant and his wound?

A. They are concerned and sorry.

B. They are irritated and impatient.

C. They are efficient and helpful.

D. They are confused and slow.

___ 10. What does the author mean by this passage from "An Episode of War"?

"Let go of me," said the lieutenant, holding back wrathfully, his glance fixed upon the door of the old schoolhouse, as sinister to him as the portals of death.

A. The lieutenant almost died in elementary school.

B. The lieutenant fears dying in the army hospital.

C. The lieutenant's schoolhouse was always scary to him.

D. The lieutenant knows the schoolhouse is overcrowded.

Vocabulary and Grammar

___ 11. In which sentence is the meaning of the word *compelled* expressed?

A. The lieutenant wondered who had shot him.

B. The cries of the men and horses were wild.

C. The men insisted the lieutenant get his wound treated.

D. The doctors were unsympathetic to the lieutenant's state.

___ 12. Which of the following is correctly capitalized?

A. the Civil War

B. the civil war

C. the civil War

D. the Civil war

Essay

13. In "An Episode of War," the lieutenant's comrades are sympathetic to him when he is wounded. On the other hand, the medical staff is not. Why do you think this is so? Write a brief essay giving your ideas about why Crane portrayed the two sets of characters in this way.

14. What would be a reasonable purpose for reading "An Episode of War?" Why might you suggest it to someone as an important piece of writing? Write a brief essay, and give examples from the story to support your choice of a reading purpose.

Name _____ Date _____

Selection Test B

Critical Reading *Identify the letter of the choice that best completes the statement or answers the question.*

____ 1. Which of the following reasons would cause you to set a slow reading rate for the following passage from "An Episode of War"?

> He was on the verge of a great triumph in mathematics, and the corporals were thronging forward, each to reap a little square, when suddenly the lieutenant cried out and looked quickly at a man near him as if he suspected it was a case of personal assault.

    I. long sentence
    II. difficult vocabulary
    III. wartime setting
    IV. several phrases
    A. I, II, III
    B. II, III, IV
    C. I, II, IV
    D. I, III, IV

____ 2. In "An Episode of War," what is the lieutenant doing just before he is shot?
    A. drinking coffee with his men
    B. dividing the coffee among his men
    C. reading a mathematics book
    D. aiming his gun at an enemy soldier

____ 3. Which of the following might you read for the same purpose as you set for reading "An Episode of War"?
    A. an essay on warfare
    B. a book of maps and descriptions of Revolutionary War battles
    C. a collection of letters home from Civil War soldiers
    D. a survey of disease mortality in Civil War soldiers

____ 4. Why are the soldiers all so astonished when their lieutenant is shot in "An Episode of War"?
    A. They have been well hidden.
    B. They are asleep when it happens.
    C. They are all using swords.
    D. They are not in the middle of battle.

____ 5. In "An Episode of War," why do the lieutenant's comrades act the way they do after he is shot?
    A. They are annoyed to lose their coffee.
    B. They are angry at the enemy.
    C. They feel lucky that they were spared.
    D. They feel that he has become special.

_____ 6. Why does the lieutenant act puzzled about what to do with his sword after he is shot?
A. He cannot lift his sword any more.
B. He cannot respond to a bullet wound with a sword.
C. He still has the coffee to divide among the men.
D. He does not know where he should put the sword.

_____ 7. Stephen Crane's fascination with the Civil War was one of the influences on his life and his writing. Read this passage from "An Episode of War." Which of the following facts contributed to Crane's writing of this passage?

A wound gives strange dignity to him who bears it. . . . His comrades look at him with large eyes thoughtfully.

A. Crane was born after the end of the Civil War.
B. Army field hospitals were filthy and crowded.
C. Crane interviewed Civil War veterans about being wounded.
D. Many wounded men lost their arms or legs.

_____ 8. Stephen Crane's fascination with the Civil War was one of the influences on his life and his writing. Read this passage from "An Episode of War." Which of the following facts contributed to the writing of this passage?

He came upon some stragglers, and they told him how to find the field hospital. They described its exact location.

A. Stephen Crane died of tuberculosis at age 28.
B. Stephen Crane was a reporter before he wrote fiction.
C. Stephen Crane studied maps of how battle areas were set up.
D. Stephen Crane changed the way readers viewed war.

_____ 9. Which of these facts contributed to Stephen Crane's writing of this passage from "An Episode of War"?

A battery, a tumultuous and shining mass, was swirling toward the right. The wild thud of hoofs, the cries of the riders shouting blame and praise, menace and encouragement . . . brought the lieutenant to an intent pause.

A. Crane was fascinated by the Civil War.
B. Many soldiers lost their limbs from wounds.
C. Civil War army field hospitals were filthy.
D. Crane read firsthand accounts of the fighting.

_____ 10. What can you conclude about the state of medical care during the Civil War from this passage?

An interminable crowd of bandaged men were coming and going. Great numbers sat under the trees nursing heads or arms or legs.

A. The most common wartime injuries were to the head, arms, or legs.
B. Army hospitals were so crowded that many wounded stayed outside.
C. Only bandaged soldiers were allowed to leave the hospital.
D. Wounded soldiers often had to return for more treatment.

____ 11. How does the soldier in "An Episode of War" act when he finally reaches his home?
   A. ashamed for being wounded
   B. angry for having lost his arm
   C. pleased to see his family's concern
   D. sorry he went to war in the first place

____ 12. What purpose would you set for reading further after reading this passage?

> "I guess I won't have it amputated," he said.
>
> "Nonsense, man! Nonsense! Nonsense! cried the doctor. "Come along, now. I won't amputate it. Come along. Don't be a baby."

   A. to learn whether the lieutenant's arm was amputated
   B. to learn whether the lieutenant ended up going home
   C. to find out what surgical techniques the doctor used
   D. to find out if the doctor was good at his job

Vocabulary and Grammar

____ 13. In which sentence is the meaning of the word *compelled* expressed?
   A. The men were too nervous to touch their wounded lieutenant.
   B. They helped him sheathe his sword in its scabbard.
   C. The lieutenant was driven to defend himself to the doctor.
   D. The lieutenant's family agonized over his lost arm.

____ 14. Which of the following is capitalized correctly?
   A. The writing of Stephen Crane is realistic.
   B. The Writing of Stephen Crane is realistic.
   C. The writing of stephen crane is realistic.
   D. The Writing of Stephen Crane is Realistic.

____ 15. Which of the following sentences is correctly capitalized?
   A. The soldiers stared at the Officer.
   B. The Soldiers stared at the officer.
   C. The soldiers stared at the officer.
   D. the soldiers stared at the officer.

Essay

16. Stephen Crane's writings on war are realistic and descriptive. They show wartime from the point of view of the ordinary soldier. How else is war portrayed in books, movies, and video games? Write a brief essay that compares Crane's view of war in "An Episode of War," with another point of view about war with which you are familiar.

17. The central event in "An Episode of War" is the lieutenant's wound and what happens afterward. What is unexpected about this situation? Write a brief essay that explains why certain parts of this story are not what a reader might expect.

Vocabulary Warm-up Word Lists

Study these words from the selections. Then, complete the activities.

Word List A

beacons [BEE kuhnz] *n.* lights used to guide ships and planes
   Along the rocky New England coast, <u>beacons</u> help keep ships safe.

betrayed [bi TRAYD] *v.* broke someone's trust in you
   I <u>betrayed</u> Adam by keeping my party a secret from him.

collectors [cuh LEK tuhrz] *n.* people who gather and keep things
   Can you believe that those <u>collectors</u> bought our old vases?

discovering [dis KUH ver ing] *n.* the act of finding out something
   We tried to find ways of <u>discovering</u> the secret entrance to the house.

enabled [en AY buhld] *v.* made someone or something possible
   That television show <u>enabled</u> regular people to become stars.

involved [in VAHLVD] *adj.* taking part in something
   If you were <u>involved</u> in this surprise, thank you!

phrases [FRAYZ ez] *n.* groups of words with special meaning
   My favorite singer uses <u>phrases</u> that seem to be written just for me.

topic [TAHP ik] *n.* the subject of a piece of writing
   My English teacher thought that I should narrow the <u>topic</u> of my essay.

Word List B

basic [BAY sik] *adj.* at the simplest level
   The school did not have even <u>basic</u> supplies such as chalkboard erasers.

inappropriate [in uh PROH pree it] *adj.* not right for a time or place
   Wearing a hat during the Pledge of Allegiance is always <u>inappropriate</u>.

miniature [MIN ee uh cher] *adj.* very small
   The <u>miniature</u> shoe fit easily in the palm of my hand.

obnoxious [uhb NAHK shuhs] *adj.* very rude and unpleasant
   An <u>obnoxious</u> look on your face can be worse than rude words.

reveal [ri VEEL] *v.* to make known; to show
   I never like to <u>reveal</u> my true feelings to anyone but good friends.

sorrowful [SAHR uh fuhl] *adj.* filled with great sadness
   The <u>sorrowful</u> song on the radio made me feel like crying.

tempt [TEMPT] *v.* to try to get someone to do something
   The chocolates could not <u>tempt</u> Alan to break his vow not to eat sweets.

unique [yoo NEEK] *adj.* being the only one of its kind
   The <u>unique</u> color of her eyes had yellow mixed in with brown.

from **My Own True Name** by Pat Mora
"Words to Sit In, Like Chairs" by Naomi Shihab Nye
Vocabulary Warm-up Exercises

Exercise A *Fill in each blank in the paragraph below with an appropriate word from Word List A. Use each word only once.*

Last year, our school speech team won at the state level. I was not

[1] _____ except as part of the audience. This year, my schedule

has [2] _____ me to join the team. I am in the process of

[3] _____ all kinds of things about being an effective speaker. If I feel

nervous, for example, I pretend that two bright [4] _____ are just over

the judges' heads, guiding me. I have also learned that each of my words and every

one of my [5] _____ must be carefully written and revised. Each

team member chose a speech [6] _____ for the year. We all became

[7] _____ of interesting facts for one another. I have chosen to speak

about people in history who have been [8] _____ by their governments.

Exercise B *Answer each question. Use a word from Word List B to replace each underlined word or group of words without changing the meaning.*

Example: What makes giraffes such <u>special</u> animals?
Giraffes are <u>unique</u> animals because of their long necks.

1. What is an event that has caused several of your friends to have <u>unhappy</u> expressions on their faces at the same time?

   _____

2. What is a <u>simple</u> rule people should follow to avoid being <u>rude</u>?

   _____

3. What <u>tiny</u> version of some object do you own?

   _____

4. How do award shows build excitement before they <u>make known</u> the winners?

   _____

5. Why is it <u>wrong</u> to open other people's mail?

   _____

6. What do all advertisements <u>try to get</u> you to do?

   _____

Name _____ Date _____

from **My Own True Name** by Pat Mora
"Words to Sit In, Like Chairs" by Naomi Shihab Nye
Reading Warm-up A

Read the following passage. Pay special attention to the underlined words. Then, read it again, and complete the activities. Use a separate sheet of paper for your written answers.

So you want to be a professional writer? Get ready for some hard work and some rude awakenings! Writing for a living might sound like fun. However, many who have gotten <u>involved</u> in this profession have failed or quit. Writing for money means much more than having a good idea or being able to craft perfect <u>phrases</u>. Writing for a living means that you get up every day and write—no matter how uninspired you might be feeling!

The most successful writers follow a routine. They know they must keep trying to put words on paper every day, even if they feel blocked. That's right! Creativity and ease of words, usually a true writer's best friends, have <u>betrayed</u> every writer at one time or another. Experienced writers plod along through these difficult times, somehow <u>discovering</u> again along the way the voice that they had lost.

Professional writers also know that they might not always be able to write about a favorite <u>topic</u>. Sure, one writer might love music. Another writer might dream of writing a best-selling novel. Unfortunately, what will pay the rent might be an article about lighthouse <u>beacons</u> along the Oregon coast. Happily, most good writers eventually are <u>enabled</u> by their talent to write mostly about ideas close to their hearts.

Finally, the most successful writers become <u>collectors</u> of useful names, e-mail addresses, and phone numbers. Writers cannot simply focus on being creative. To survive, they must also regularly promote themselves and their work by talking to and meeting with others. Until authors hit it big and hire agents, they must be their own best advertisers. Even as they work on one piece of writing, they are constantly looking for the next assignment.

Are you still interested in being a professional writer? Then, grab a pen and notebook, or sit down at the computer, and begin writing.

1. Underline the words that tell what many people <u>involved</u> in professional writing have done. Tell about something you are *involved* in that you enjoy.

2. Circle the adjective describing <u>phrases</u>. Then, explain what *phrases* are.

3. Underline the words naming what has <u>betrayed</u> every writer. Explain why the author compared these things to friends in the same sentence in which she used *betrayed*.

4. Circle the words naming what writers are in the process of <u>discovering</u>. Tell about something you are now in the process of *discovering*.

5. Underline the word in the next sentence that identifies one writer's favorite <u>topic</u>. Name a *topic* you like to read or write about.

6. Circle the word that helps to explain <u>beacons</u>. Write a description of what the *beacons* might look like.

7. Explain how being *collectors* of useful names has *enabled* writers to survive in their profession.

Name _____ Date _____

from **My Own True Name** by Pat Mora
Reading Warm-up B

Read the following passage. Pay special attention to the underlined words. Then, read it again, and complete the activities. Use a separate sheet of paper for your written answers.

In 1791, the Congress of the young United States passed the Bill of Rights. These ten amendments guarantee the most <u>basic</u> rights Americans have as citizens of a free country. For example, we can choose our own religion. We are not forced to keep soldiers in our homes during wartime. We have the right to a speedy and fair trial if accused of a crime. We can tell our leaders what we think is wrong with government.

For people who make their living as writers, the First Amendment in the Bill of Rights is especially important. It states: "Congress shall make no law . . . abridging the freedom of speech, or of the press. . . ." Clearly, the founding fathers knew it would be <u>inappropriate</u> for the government to make laws restricting what people say or write.

In the United States, writers do not fear for their lives because of what they write. Here, journalists are free to publish their findings, no matter who might look bad as a result. In addition, reporters do not have to <u>reveal</u> their sources. We should never forget how <u>unique</u> these freedoms are in a world often filled with restrictions.

We should thank the framers of the Constitution. Because of their wisdom, United States leaders have avoided the pitfalls of too much power that often <u>tempt</u> rulers in other types of government. We have not had <u>sorrowful</u> scenes in our country such as book burnings, or the murder of writers who have spoken against the government.

Of course, not everything that is published in the United States is considered great writing. Some work can only be described as <u>obnoxious</u>. Some pieces of writing are completely uninteresting. Still, each piece should be seen as a victory, a <u>miniature</u> representation of a great freedom.

1. Underline the words naming what gives us <u>basic</u> rights. Describe a *basic* right you think is especially important.

2. Circle the words describing what the founding fathers found <u>inappropriate</u>. Describe an *inappropriate* use of power you have seen.

3. Underline the words naming what reporters do not have to <u>reveal</u>. Explain what *reveal* means.

4. Circle the words naming what is <u>unique</u>. Explain how our *unique* freedoms can result in *obnoxious* writing.

5. Underline the words naming what can <u>tempt</u> rulers. Why might power *tempt* all types of people to misuse it?

6. Circle the words that name <u>sorrowful</u> scenes. Choose one, and describe why you think it is the most *sorrowful* one listed.

7. Describe something that you know that can be a *miniature* representation of a freedom.

Name _____ Date _____

from **My Own True Name** by Pat Mora
"Words to Sit In, Like Chairs" by Naomi Shihab Nye
Literary Analysis: Comparing Works on a Similar Theme

The **theme** of a literary work is the insight, major idea, or underlying message that it communicates. Certain themes are common across cultures and historical eras. These recurring ideas are known as **universal themes** because they appear in many cultures. Examples of universal themes include the power of love and the importance of freedom.

The excerpt from *My Own True Name* and "Words to Sit In, Like Chairs" both take as their theme the importance of self-expression. Even when two authors choose to write on a similar theme, they frequently produce different results. The reason is that writers draw on different life experiences, use different structures, have different opinions, and explore different aspects of the same theme.

DIRECTIONS: *Answer the following questions about the presentation of theme in these two works.*

From *My Own True Name*	Questions	"Words to Sit In, Like Chairs"
	1. What literary form did each writer choose to use?	
	2. How does each writer's choice of literary form affect his or her presentation of the theme?	
	3. What is each writer's theme?	
	4. What main points does each writer make about the theme?	
	5. What are the similarities in the two writers' approaches to the theme?	
	6. What are the differences in the two writers' approaches to the theme?	

from **My Own True Name** by Pat Mora
"Words to Sit In, Like Chairs" by Naomi Shihab Nye
Vocabulary Builder

A. DIRECTIONS: *Find a synonym or definition as directed for each vocabulary word below. Then, use the vocabulary word in a sentence that makes the meaning of the word clear.*

1. **Vocabulary Word:** intimidating   **Synonym:** _____

   Sample Sentence: _____

2. **Vocabulary Word:** bilingual   **Definition:** _____

   Sample Sentence: _____

3. **Vocabulary Word:** eavesdropping   **Definition:** _____

   Sample Sentence: _____

4. **Vocabulary Word:** soberly   **Synonym:** _____

   Sample Sentence: _____

5. **Vocabulary Word:** turmoil   **Synonym:** _____

   Sample Sentence: _____

6. **Vocabulary Word:** beacons   **Synonym:** _____

   Sample Sentence: _____

B. DIRECTIONS: *Circle the letter of the word that is most* opposite *in meaning to the word in CAPITAL LETTERS.*

1. SOBERLY
   A. loudly
   B. seriously
   C. flippantly
   D. conscientiously

2. TURMOIL
   A. heartache
   B. confusion
   C. trouble
   D. calm

3. INTIMIDATING
   A. bulldozing
   B. welcoming
   C. smiling
   D. counting

4. BEACONS
   A. darkness
   B. light
   C. runway
   D. warning

Name _____ Date _____

from **My Own True Name** by Pat Mora
"Words to Sit In, Like Chairs" by Naomi Shihab Nye

Support for Writing to Compare Multiple Works on a Similar Theme

Before you write your essay comparing and contrasting the excerpt from *My Own True Nature* and "Words to Sit In, Like Chairs," use the graphic organizer below to list ideas about how each author develops the theme of self-expression and its importance.

From *My Own True Name* and "Words to Sit In, Like Chairs"

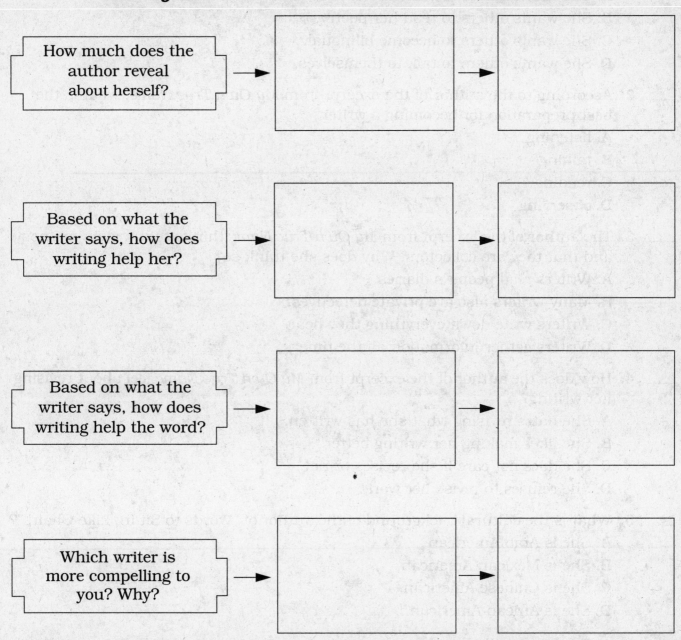

How much does the author reveal about herself?

Based on what the writer says, how does writing help her?

Based on what the writer says, how does writing help the word?

Which writer is more compelling to you? Why?

Now, use your notes to write your essay comparing and contrasting the development of theme in these two works.

from **My Own True Name** by Pat Mora
"Words to Sit In, Like Chairs" by Naomi Shihab Nye
Selection Test A

Critical Reading *Identify the letter of the choice that best answers the question.*

____ 1. Why is the author of the excerpt from *My Own True Name* writing to her "fellow writer"?
A. She wants others to write more.
B. She wants others to read her poetry.
C. She wants others to become bilingual.
D. She wants others to talk to themselves.

____ 2. According to the author of the excerpt from *My Own True Name*, what is the best preparation for becoming a writer?
A. listening
B. talking
C. reading
D. observing

____ 3. The author of the excerpt from *My Own True Name* thinks that writers are nosy and that they are collectors. Why does she think so?
A. Writers read people's diaries.
B. Many writers also are private detectives.
C. Writers write down everything they hear.
D. Writers gather information all the time.

____ 4. How does the author of the excerpt from *My Own True Name* feel about revising her writing?
A. She hates revising what she has written.
B. She likes making her writing better.
C. She does not care if she revises or not.
D. She refuses to revise her work.

____ 5. What is the cultural background of the author of "Words to Sit In, Like Chairs"?
A. She is Arab American.
B. She is Mexican American.
C. She is Chinese American.
D. She is African American.

_____ 6. What historical event is the author of "Words to Sit In, Like Chairs" responding to?
   A. the bombing of Pearl Harbor
   B. the Oklahoma City bombing
   C. the 2001 attack on the World Trade Center
   D. the assassination of President Kennedy

_____ 7. What helps the author of "Words to Sit In, Like Chairs" get through a tragedy?
   A. using words
   B. talking to friends
   C. writing in a notebook
   D. telling positive stories

_____ 8. In "Words to Sit In, Like Chairs," what shine "as miniature beacons, from under heaps of leaves"?
   A. her thoughts about other tragedies
   B. friends whom she could call and talk to
   C. the thoughts she had written down
   D. her feelings of turmoil

_____ 9. How is the excerpt from *My Own True Name* similar to "Words to Sit In, Like Chairs"?
   A. Both are written by Mexican Americans.
   B. Both are a piece of a larger work.
   C. Both deal with tragedies in life.
   D. Both discuss the value of self-expression.

_____ 10. How is the literary form of the excerpt from *My Own True Name* different from the form of "Words to Sit In, Like Chairs"?
   A. One is a letter and the other an essay.
   B. One is an essay and the other a narrative.
   C. One is a letter and the other a narrative.
   D. They are both narrative essays.

_____ 11. What is one of Mora's reasons for writing the excerpt from *My Own True Name*?
   A. to tell others to read and be inspired by her book of poetry
   B. to encourage others to write in order to know themselves better
   C. to encourage students to read and write more in school
   D. to tell other writers several secrets of writers and to give them tips

____ 12. What is one of Naomi Shihab Nye's main reasons for writing "Words to Sit In,
Like Chairs"?

    A. to tell others what she felt when she first heard about a tragedy

    B. to describe for others what is is like to live in America

    C. to encourage others to express their thoughts and feelings with words

    D. to share with others her solution for violence in the world

Vocabulary

____ 13. How many languages does a *bilingual* person speak?

    A. one

    B. two

    C. three

    D. four

____ 14. Which of the following means the same as *turmoil*?

    A. storm

    B. tumble

    C. tranquility

    D. unrest

____ 15. Which word is most similar in meaning to *soberly*?

    A. excitedly

    B. consistently

    C. thoughtfully

    D. considerately

Essay

16. Imagine that Pat Mora, the writer of the excerpt from *My Own True Name*, and
Naomi Shihab Nye, the writer of "Words to Sit In, Like Chairs" could spend some
time together. In a brief essay, tell at least two things they would probably say to
each other about writing and whether they would agree or disagree.

17. Authors often use personal experience in their writing. In an essay, identify the personal experiences Mora and Nye write about in the pieces you read—the excerpt
from *My Own True Name* and "Words to Sit In, Like Chairs."

from **My Own True Name** by Pat Mora
"Words to Sit In, Like Chairs" by Naomi Shihab Nye
Selection Test B

Critical Reading *Identify the letter of the choice that best answers the question.*

____ 1. Why does the author of the excerpt from *My Own True Name* think writing is important?
A. Writing helps improve reading skills.
B. Writing helps you discover yourself.
C. Writing is important to communication.
D. Writing is something we all have to do.

____ 2. Which of the following are reasons the author of the excerpt from *My Own True Name* gives for not writing regulary until she was older?
   I.   She did not think she had anything important to say.
   II. She did not believe that she could say anything well.
   III. She did not have time write because she was in school and working.
   IV. In school, she never studied a writer who was like her, a Mexican American.
A. I, II, III   B. II, III, IV   C. I, II, IV   D. I, III, IV

____ 3. What does the following line from *My Own True Name* mean?
   . . . some writers are quiet and shy, others noisy. . . . Some write quickly, and some are as slow as an elderly man struggling up a steep hill on a windy day.

A. Writers have their own styles of writing.
B. Writers have different personalities.
C. Writers are different ages.
D. Writers are usually elderly people.

____ 4. Why does the author of *My Own True Name* say that writers are "usually nosy and very good at eavesdropping"?
A. Writers are not good at keeping secrets.
B. Many writers are also private detectives.
C. Writers interrupt others' conversations.
D. Writers are always gathering information.

____ 5. How does writing help the author discover her "own true name" in the excerpt from *My Own True Name*?
A. Writing helps her discover the world.
B. Writing helps her know herself better.
C. Writing helps her live with her heritage.
D. Writing helps her like who she is.

____ 6. On September 11, 2001, why does the boy think the Collapse-It laundry basket may be an inappropriate gift for the author of "Words to Sit In, Like Chairs"?
A. The Twin Towers have just collapsed, and the laundry basket is a reminder of it.
B. An object like a laundry basket seems silly in the face of great tragedy.
C. The boy realizes a laundry basket is not a very good gift.
D. No one else gives Nye a gift, so the boy feels he did the wrong thing.

_____ 7. To help her through tragedy, the author of "Words to Sit In, Like Chairs" uses
   A. friends
   B. words
   C. stories
   D. gifts

_____ 8. What sorrows does the author of "Words to Sit In, Like Chairs" refer to when she says that she and her Arab American friends "shared a doubled sense of sorrow"?
   A. sorrow for the Arabs and Americans who died in the Twin Towers's collapse
   B. sorrow over September 11 and sorrow for what would happen as a result
   C. sorrow for those who died and sorrow that the hijackers were Arabs
   D. sorrow that the hijackers were Arab and sorrow for how people will treat Arabs

_____ 9. How did speaking with others and writing about the tragedy affect the author of "Words to Sit In, Like Chairs"?
   A. Speaking and writing helped her sort through her emotions of anger and hurt.
   B. Speaking and writing helped her to ease the sorrow.
   C. Speaking and writing helped her to express herself to the public.
   D. Speaking and writing helped her to ease the pain of others.

_____ 10. *My Own True Name* is similar to "Words to Sit In, Like Chairs" because
   A. both are written by Mexican Americans.
   B. both are part of larger work.
   C. both deal with a tragedy that occurred during the writer's lifetime.
   D. both discuss the importance of self-expression.

_____ 11. Which is true of *My Own True Name* and "Words to Sit In, Like Chairs"?
   A. Both are fiction.
   B. Both are nonfiction.
   C. Both are narrative essays.
   D. Both are descriptive essays.

_____ 12. How does Mora tie her theme to her experience in *My Own True Name*?
   A. She discusses how writing has been difficult for her as a bilingual person.
   B. She describes how her aunt was an American Indian storyteller.
   C. She explains how diverse she is by liking enchiladas and sushi.
   D. She tells how reading and writing has always been a part of her life.

_____ 13. How does Nye tie her theme to her experience in "Words to Sit In, Like Chairs"?
   A. She tells how her students treated her unfairly after September 11, 2001.
   B. She describes what she thought, felt, and experienced after September 11, 2001.
   C. She explains how her poet friend in New York responded to September 11, 2001.
   D. She compares her feelings of despair to the collapsible laundry basket.

_____ 14. Mora's goal in writing the piece from *My Own True Name* is
   A. to teach readers how to write.
   B. to encourage to study harder.
   C. to encourage others to write as a means of self-discovery.
   D. to reflect on the meaning of September 11, 2001.

____ 15. Naomi Shihab Nye's goal in writing "Words to Sit In, Like Chairs" is
    A. to explain how words, like chairs, can be comfortable and supportive.
    B. to tell others what she felt when she first heard about September 11, 2001.
    C. to describe her childhood in Texas.
    D. to describe the memorial for victims of a tragedy in Oklahoma.

Vocabulary

____ 16. In which sentence is *intimidating* used correctly?
    A. The cat's purr was intimidating to the mail carrier approaching the house.
    B. The comprehensive standardized test was intimidating to the elementary students.
    C. The lanky running back was intimidating to the large, experienced defensive lineman.
    D. The field of pretty flowers was intimidating to the group of kids on a picnic.

____ 17. A person who is *bilingual* can
    A. read and speak one language.
    B. read and speak two languages.
    C. read and speak many languages.
    D. read many languages, but speak only one.

____ 18. An antonym for *turmoil* is
    A. storm
    B. tumble
    C. unrest
    D. tranquility

____ 19. Which word or phrase is most *similar* in meaning to *soberly*?
    A. somberly
    B. drunkenly
    C. in an arrogant way
    D. in a serious, dignified way

Essay

20. The theme of a literary work is the major idea or underlying message that it communicates. Write an essay about the themes of the excerpt from *My Own True Name* and of "Words to Sit In, Like Chairs." What is the theme in each work? What are the similarities in the authors' ideas? What are the differences in the authors' ideas? What did each author's ideas cause you to think about the theme?

21. In an essay, discuss how the literary forms Mora and Nye use in, respectively, the piece from *My Own True Name* and "Words to Sit In, Like Chairs" affect the way each writer presents her message.

22. Write an essay comparing the excerpt from *My Own True Name* and "Words to Sit in, Like Chairs" by answering these questions: How much does each author reveal about herself and her reasons for writing? How does writing help her? How, according to each author, can writing help the world? Which writer do you find more compelling or persuasive? Why?

Writing Workshop—Unit 6, Part 2
Exposition: Cause-and-Effect Essay

Prewriting: Using Self-Interview

To find topics that interest you, ask yourself the questions below and then choose the one that interests you the most.

What is my favorite book? What natural or historical events are crucial to the story?	
What interesting facts have I learned in science class?	
Which political leader do I admire most? What was happening in the world when he or she was in office?	

Drafting: Organizing Your Ideas

Use the appropriate graphic organizer below to choose which description best fits your topic as well as to organize your causes and effects.

Many Cause/Single Effect

First Cause   Second Cause   Third Cause   Single Effect

Single Causes/Many Effects

Single Cause   First Effect   Second Effect   Third Effect

Chain of Causes and Effects

Single Cause   Single Effect   Single Cause   Single Effect

Writing Workshop—Unit 6, Part 2
Cause-and-Effect Essay: Integrating Grammar Skills

Revising to Use Quotation Marks and Block Quotes

When you use quotations, you must set them off so your reader knows they are someone else's words. Introduce a long quotation of five or more lines with a colon and indent the entire quotation on the left. Do not use quotation marks for the quote. Shorter quotations of five or fewer lines of text are treated like the quotations in the dialogue of a story. Use quotation marks and commas to separate the quotation from the rest of a sentence.

> According to the story, the house in which Helen Stoner lived was in some disrepair, "the roof was partly caved in, a picture of ruin."

Identifying When to Use Quotation Marks and Block Quotes

A. DIRECTIONS: *Below is a quote that is written incorrectly. On the lines, explain how you would correct the passage.*

Abraham Lincoln's Gettysburg Address begins with these words: "Fourscore and seven years ago our fathers brought forth on this continent a new nation conceived in liberty and dedicated to the proposition that all men are created equal. Now we are engaged in a great civil war testing whether that nation, or any nation so conceived and so dedicated, can long endure. We are met on a great battlefield of that war. We have come to dedicate a portion of that field as a final resting-place for those who here gave their lives that that nation might live."

_____

_____

Fixing Incorrect Use of Quotations

B. DIRECTIONS: *Rewrite the two quotes below so that they are written correctly.*

1. In a debate with Stephen Douglas, Abraham Lincoln said:
   A house divided against itself cannot stand.

_____

_____

2. In his Inaugural Address on March 4, 1861, Abraham Lincoln said:
   . . . the Union of these States is perpetual.

_____

_____

Spelling Workshop—Unit 6
Vowel Sounds in Unstressed Syllables

The **vowels in unstressed syllables** often do not have a clear, distinguishable sound. Notice, for example, how the *ie* in *deficient* sounds the same as the *ai* in *politician*. This unclear vowel sound can occur in more than one syllable in a word and can be spelled by any vowel or combination of vowels.

Word List

accurate	evidence	magnificent	politician
deficient	leisure	mediocre	semester

A. DIRECTIONS: *Write the word from the Word List that matches each clue.*

1. one half of a school year _____
2. person who works in government _____
3. neither very good nor very bad _____
4. something used to prove a case _____
5. wonderful; marvelous _____
6. opposite of work _____
7. lacking _____
8. precise and correct _____

B. DIRECTIONS: *Write three sentences about each topic below. Use every list word at least once.*

1. the difference between a good and bad vacation

_____

_____

_____

2. how a student can improve his or her grades

_____

_____

_____

3. the candidate you would support in the next local election

_____

_____

_____

Name _____ Date _____

Delivering a Persuasive Speech Using Media

After choosing a topic about your school, fill out the following chart to help you organize and present your infomercial.

Topic of presentation: _____

Write a single statement to express your main idea.
What primary and secondary sources are you using to support your ideas?
What media sources are you using to emphasize your points?
What equipment will you need for your presentation?
What persuasive arguments are you using to convince the audience to agree with your position?

For Further Reading—Unit 6

DIRECTIONS: *Think about the books you have read. Then, on a separate sheet of paper, answer the discussion questions and take notes for your Literature Circle.*

Eagle Song by Joseph Bruchac

Discussion Do you think life in a city is easy for the Bigtree family? Explain your answer with support from the story.

Connections—Literature Circle What does Richard Bigtree mean when he says, "It takes a lot more courage to make a friend than it does to make an enemy"? Do you think Danny is courageous when he asks Tyrone for his friendship? Explain your answer.

Immigrant Voices: Twenty-four Narratives on Becoming an American edited by Gordon Hutner

Discussion In 1890, Jacob Riis published *How the Other Half Lives.* What social ills did this book expose? Why do you think Riis's book was more effective than his speeches and articles?

Connections—Literature Circle Cite two examples of figurative language that Ernesto Galarza uses to create a vivid image of the barrio from *Barrio Boy.* Give two examples showing how the principal and teachers at the Lincoln School supported cultural diversity among students.

Ashanti to Zulu: African Traditions by Margaret Musgrove

Discussion Choose the tradition that corresponds to the first letter of your first name. For example, if your name is Sam or Sue, you would choose the Sotho tradition. Speculate about the way the tradition reflects what is important in the culture.

Connection—Literary Circle There are usually very practical reasons for traditions and customs. Speculate on how one or two of the customs described in this book might have come into being. Then examine a custom or tradition in your culture. Is there a practical reason for the tradition's existence?

All Quiet on the Western Front by Erich Maria Remarque

Discussion How does Paul learn that the enemy is not just faceless, nameless people? Explain.

Connections—Literature Circle Describe the relationship Paul has with his friends and contrast this with the relationship he has with his family.

Unit 6: Themes in American Stories
Part 2 Benchmark Test 12

MULTIPLE CHOICE

Reading Skill

1. When should you set a purpose for reading?
   A. before you read
   B. after you finish reading
   C. only when you read to be entertained
   D. only when you read to be informed

2. When you set a purpose for reading, what should you put in the first column of a *K-W-L* chart?
   A. what you already **k**now about the topic
   B. what you want to **k**now about the topic
   C. what you **k**eep reading about the topic
   D. a **k**ey sentence about the topic

3. Once you set a purpose for reading, what should you do about your rate of reading?
   A. Adjust your rate of reading to match your mood.
   B. Read more slowly when you enjoy what you are reading.
   C. Read more slowly when you are reading to learn new information.
   D. Always read at the same speed, no matter what you are reading.

Read this selection. Then, answer the questions that follow.

(1) In the days of the Wright brothers, scientists expected that a man would fly-not the Wright brothers, but a prominent scientist, Samuel Pierpont Langley. (2) Langley had a whole team of other scientists working with him. (3) Working in the Washington, DC, area, he built a series of experimental flying machines. (4) Wilbur and Orville Wright, in contrast, had no formal scientific training. (5) To earn a living, they ran a bicycle shop in their home town. (6) Intrigued by the possibility of flight, they studied aerodynamics, built their flying machine, and flew it successfully. (7) Even after their landmark success, it took years for them to get credit for the achievement.

4. Which of these is a likely purpose you might have for reading the selection?
   A. to learn about the history of Washington, D.C.
   B. to learn the history of Dayton, Ohio
   C. to learn about the early history of flying
   D. to learn the laws of aerodynamics

5. Along with finding out facts, which purpose might you have for reading this selection?
   A. to investigate products before buying them
   B. to escape to an imaginary world of adventure
   C. to be entertained with amusing historical anecdotes
   D. to appreciate the poetry written about flying

6. Imagine that you were writing a paper on people other than the Wright Brothers who tried to develop early flying machines. What would you most likely do?
   A. Take notes on sentences 1 through 3 only.
   B. Take notes on sentences 4 through 7 only.
   C. Take notes on the whole selection.
   D. Read the selection quickly.

7. Which question would most help you set a purpose for reading the selection?
   A. What did the Wright Brothers' airplane look like?
   B. Why did scientists not believe flight was possible?
   C. How were airplanes important to military technology?
   D. What was unusual about the Wright Brothers' achievement?

8. What is a transcript?
   A. a complete written record of a spoken event
   B. a written summary of a spoken event
   C. a paraphrase that restates people's words in simpler language
   D. a commentary on a spoken event

9. For which of these events are people most likely to want transcripts?
   A. a commercial on TV or radio
   B. a public affairs program on TV
   C. a live music concert
   D. a birthday party

Literary Analysis *Read this selection. Then, answer the questions that follow.*

During the Great Depression, jobs were scarce. To keep his job, Leah's father moved his family from New York City to upstate New York. It was a shocking change for the Kaminsky family, especially Leah's mother. Living in a Jewish immigrant community, Mrs. Kaminsky had gotten by with her poor English skills for nearly twenty years. Now, in the small upstate city, she was forced to rely on her daughter to help her with everyday tasks. For Leah, being a support to her mother was gratifying. And though she did not like moving away from her friends, she liked the looks of the new school.

10. What ethnic group is featured most prominently in the cultural context of this selection?
    A. Jewish Americans
    B. Mexican Americans
    C. Italian Americans
    D. African Americans

11. How is the Kaminsky family affected by the Great Depression of the 1930s?
    A. The family is forced to immigrate to America.
    B. The family must leave their immigrant community for an unfamiliar American city.
    C. The parents have trouble putting food on the table to feed their children.
    D. Mrs. Kaminsky is forced to find a job in order to supplement her husband's income.

12. How does Mrs. Kaminsky react to the cultural and historical events that change her life?
    A. She is miserable about the loss of income and strives to regain her social status.
    B. She is upset with the changes and relies more on her daughter.
    C. She is glad to move to a place near farms like those she remembers from Europe.
    D. She makes up her mind to learn English and to adopt American ways.

13. How does Leah react to the historical and cultural events that change her life?
    A. She likes some of the changes but dislikes having to help her mother with tasks.
    B. She dislikes all the changes and especially hates the boredom of rural life.
    C. She likes some of the changes but misses her friends from New York City.
    D. She is so self absorbed that she barely notices the changes taking place around her.

Read this selection about author Agatha Christie. Then, answer the question that follow.

Born in England, Agatha Christie grew up at a time when women from wealthy families did not work for a living. World War I, however, changed all that. During the war, Christie worked at a local hospital. Then, after the war, she began to write mysteries. Her stories featuring one of two popular detectives—Hercule Poirot, an eccentric former Belgian policeman; and Miss Jane Marple, an elderly spinster. In 1930, Christie married the British archaeologist Max Malloran, whom she sometimes accompanied on his digs in the Middle East.

14. Which aspect of Agatha Christie's novels would most clearly show her cultural background?
    A. her ability to create really puzzling mysteries
    B. her portrayal of changing times in English society
    C. her portrayal of Belgian detective Hercule Poirot
    D. her detailed understanding of criminal procedures

15. How do you think Christie's war experiences helped her write mysteries?
    A. She learned about the horrors men face in battle.
    B. She learned how to make the likely person the guilty party.
    C. She obtained knowledge of wounds to use in describing crimes.
    D. She learned how the local police force worked.

16. Christie's *Death Comes as the End* is a historical mystery set in ancient Egypt. Which aspect of her background do you think probably had the most influence on this novel?
    A. the fact that she had survived World War I
    B. the fact that she came from a wealthy family and was not expected to work for a living
    C. the fact that she grew up in England
    D. the fact that she married an archaeologist and went on digs with him in the Middle East

17. What is a universal theme?
    A. an insight, major idea, or underlying message specific to a work's setting
    B. an insight, major idea, or underlying message about space exploration
    C. an insight, major idea, or underlying message about God or the afterlife
    D. an insight, major idea, or underlying message that appears in many cultures

Read these two story summaries. Then, answer the questions that follow.

Story A: A new headmaster comes to run the local school in a Nigerian village, hoping to improve the quality of life. The first thing he does is close the school to villagers who walk across the lawn to reach the local burial ground. The villagers are furious that they cannot visit their ancestors and complain to school authorities, who fire the headmaster.

Story B: A group of real-estate developers want to build a new sports stadium in an American city neighborhood. They say that the stadium will bring jobs to the neighborhood, and some politicians agree. People in the neighborhood, however, are furious, saying a stadium will change the quiet residential character of their neighborhood. The politicians back out, and the stadium project is canceled.

18. Based on the summaries, what common theme do the two stories share?
    A. Change is not always an improvement.
    B. Love of money is the root of all evil.
    C. You can't fight city hall.
    D. It is important to respect one's ancestors.

19. What is different about the way the themes of the two stories are expressed?
    A. The first story puts more emphasis on economic factors.
    B. The first story puts more emphasis on political factors.
    C. The first story puts more emphasis on social customs.
    D. The second story puts more emphasis on education.

Vocabulary

20. Which of these words comes to English from Spanish?
    A. genre
    B. boomerang
    C. balcony
    D. canyon

21. Which of these words related to cooking and food comes to English from French?
    A. chef
    B. pretzel
    C. yam
    D. bagel

22. Which English word for a wind storm do you think has its origins in the Chinese *tai-fung*, which means "big wind"?
    A. hurricane
    B. blizzard
    C. tornado
    D. typhoon

23. In Persian, *khak* means "earth." What color would you guess that *khaki* pants are?
    A. white
    B. yellow brown
    C. violet blue
    D. green

24. In Spanish, a *corro* is a circle or a ring. What part of a ranch do you think a *corral* is?
    A. the farmhouse
    B. the stable
    C. the enclosure for holding the animals
    D. the field where crops are grown

Grammar

25. Which of these sentences is punctuated correctly?
    A. My little brother lost his hat, I found it the next day.
    B. I dressed him in: a hat, gloves, and a scarf.
    C. The Lost and Found contains these items; an umbrella and five gloves.
    D. I went to the Lost and Found; the hat was there.

26. How should you correct the punctuation in this sentence?

    I looked up the word in the dictionary, the entry contained the following important information, the pronunciation, the origin, and the meaning.

    A. Change the first comma to a semicolon and the second comma to a colon.
    B. Change the first comma to a colon and the second comma to a semicolon.
    C. Add a colon after *up* and remove the comma after *information*.
    D. No changes are necessary; the sentence is correct as is.

27. Which of these sentences uses correct capitalization?
    A. Last thanksgiving my parents and i visited the City of atlanta.
    B. last thanksgiving my parents and I visited the city of atlanta.
    C. Last Thanksgiving my Parents and I visited the City of Atlanta.
    D. Last Thanksgiving my parents and I visited the city of Atlanta.

28. Which of these sentences uses correct capitalization?
    A. Yesterday Miss Duncan asked the class, "How many of you like to read poetry?"
    B. Yesterday Miss Duncan asked the class, "how many of you like to read poetry?"
    C. Yesterday miss Duncan asked the class, "how many of you like to read poetry?"
    D. Yesterday miss Duncan asked the class, "How many of you like to read poetry?"

29. When should you use quotation marks for quotations that you include in an essay?
    A. for shorter quotations only
    B. for longer quotations only
    C. whenever you quote material exactly
    D. whenever you introduce a quotation with a colon

Spelling

30. Which word is spelled correctly?
    A. sillable
    B. udjoin
    C. persue
    D. pleasant

31. In which sentence is the italic word spelled correctly?
    A. Mrs. Grant is the hospital's largest *benafactor*.
    B. Did you read the *epalogue* at the end of the novel?
    C. The 30 percent discount makes the bathing suit a real *bargain*.
    D. Do not *hesatate* to phone me if you need me.

32. What should you do to spell the italic word in this sentence correctly?

    The authors of many fine words are *unonymous*.

    A. Change the *u* to *a* and the *y* to *i*.
    B. Change the *u* to *a* and the *i* to *o*.
    C. Change the *y* to *i* and drop the first *o*.
    D. Leave the word alone; it is correct.

ESSAY

Writing

33. Think of a historical period in which you might like to set a story. Jot down three questions that you would need to answer to learn more about the cultural context of the period. Then write a short proposal of the research you would do to answer your questions.

34. Imagine that you were a guest at the funeral of a historical figure that you admire. Jot down your notes for a speech that you might have given at this person's funeral.

35. Think of something significant that has happened in the history of your region or nation or an event that was important to your heritage or ancestors. Write a cause-and-effect essay explaining this historical event.

ANSWERS

"Water Names" by Lan Samantha Chang

Vocabulary Warm-up Exercises, p. 2

A.
1. bulk
2. glittered
3. reflection
4. gorges
5. forbidden
6. rippling
7. remote
8. abruptness

B. Sample Answers
1. Lil wanted a *sleek* car so she bought one that had a smooth, graceful look.
2. Each evening when I set my alarm, I look out my window at the *blackening* sky.
3. Having *fulfilled* her wish to be a star, the Oscar-winning actress cried tears of joy.
4. Since we planned to eat the fish, we *gutted* it and put it on ice.
5. Near the river's end, you can see a huge *delta*.
6. Since Mom clearly said she wanted a black sweater with some interesting details, I bought one *flecked* with blue and red.
7. Because I had *countless* good reasons for going to the party, I made my plans to attend.
8. Anna liked her *wavy* hair, so she never tried to straighten it.

Reading Warm-up A, p. 3

Sample Answers
1. that few people ever see; *Remote* means "far away."
2. (like a jewel); *Glittered* means "shone with a sparkling light."
3. sudden flooding; An earthquake comes with *abruptness* since there is no warning and it happens suddenly.
4. (high walls); *Gorges* are deep, narrow valleys with steep sides.
5. one and a half miles wide, 610 feet tall, hold five trillion gallons of water, meet one-ninth of China's needs; The *bulk* of an object that most surprised me was the skeleton of a dinosaur that I saw at the Natural History Museum.
6. (speak out against the government); *Forbidden* means "not allowed."
7. (looking); You might see the *reflection* of your own face in the river as well as the *reflection* of the mountains towering above it.

Reading Warm-up B, p. 4

Sample Answers
1. stories of his childhood in China; *Countless* means "very many."
2. (rice farming); A *delta* is a low, triangle-shaped piece of land where a river divides before emptying into the sea
3. graceful curves and bends; I once saw a beautiful, ocean-going boat with a *sleek* design.
4. *Wavy* water has water that comes up to form whitecaps or waves whereas *wavy* hair has a little bit of curl.
5. (gold); The material on our sofa is *flecked* with red and yellow.
6. (fish); If I have *gutted* a fish, then I have taken out its insides.
7. *Blackening* water makes me think that the beads are black and have a sparkle to them, like water.
8. dreams; The dream that I want to be *fulfilled* is to be a doctor who takes care of children.

Lan Samantha Chang

Listening and Viewing, p. 5

Segment 1. As a young person, Chang practiced music every day. Later, she learned to bring that discipline to her writing; music also taught her an understanding of rhythm, sound, and the buildup of excitement. Students may suggest that it is important to practice writing in order to improve one's ability to write and in order to get beyond the fear of having nothing to say.

Segment 2. Many people in China could not read or write, so they told stories to one another in order to pass down information, myths, and ideas on how to live. Students may answer that tales address complex issues, ask important questions (sometimes unanswerable), and can help a reader learn more about culture, heritage, and ancestry.

Segment 3. Chang tries to make "a riddle out of an answer" by exploring a problem or question from different sides and figuring out what the nature of the problem is instead of providing an easy answer. Students may suggest that writing about a challenging topic will help them learn more as they research facts, explore different sides of an argument, and express the issue in their own way.

Segment 4. Her stories about immigrant experiences have given voice to her own family and can resonate with families of all cultures. Students may suggest that by writing stories they could share their own feelings and ideas with others and have an impact on a reader's thoughts and opinions.

Learning About American Stories, p. 6

1. A; 2. B; 3. A; 4. C; 5. A; 6. B

"Water Names" by Lan Samantha Chang

Model Selection: American Stories, p. 7

1. Waipuo says she first heard the tale in her youth when it was told to her by her own grandmother.

2. The story is useful because it explains to the girls how their ancestors lived for generations near the river. The story also hands down to the girls one particular folk story about the river.

3. Waipuo stresses the strength and longevity of the family, which had lived for more than a thousand years near the mouth of the river. According to Waipuo, the family survived because it possessed the "spirit of the river" and recognized it must respect the water and its potential dangers.

4. Lily murmurs "a thousand years" when Waipuo introduces the story; later, she interrupts Waipuo to ask if the pearl ring came from the drowned man; and at the conclusion of the story, she asks Waipuo what happened to the beautiful girl. These interruptions help to maintain the story's suspense and to reinforce the impression that the story is part of an oral tradition involving a live audience of eager listeners.

5. Students may mention mystery, suspense, and romance as elements that kept the story alive. They also may mention the danger of desire as a theme that intrigues generation after generation. They also may mention that stories that raise questions but do not answer them tend to last a long time.

Selection Test A, p. 8

Learning About American Stories

1. ANS: B	DIF: Easy	OBJ: Literary Analysis
2. ANS: C	DIF: Easy	OBJ: Literary Analysis
3. ANS: A	DIF: Easy	OBJ: Literary Analysis
4. ANS: D	DIF: Easy	OBJ: Literary Analysis
5. ANS: C	DIF: Easy	OBJ: Literary Analysis

Critical Reading

6. ANS: D	DIF: Easy	OBJ: Comprehension
7. ANS: C	DIF: Easy	OBJ: Interpretation
8. ANS: A	DIF: Easy	OBJ: Comprehension
9. ANS: A	DIF: Easy	OBJ: Interpretation
10. ANS: B	DIF: Easy	OBJ: Interpretation
11. ANS: C	DIF: Easy	OBJ: Comprehension
12. ANS: C	DIF: Easy	OBJ: Interpretation
13. ANS: A	DIF: Easy	OBJ: Literary Analysis
14. ANS: D	DIF: Easy	OBJ: Interpretation
15. ANS: B	DIF: Easy	OBJ: Interpretation

Essay

16. In their essays, students should respond to the questions listed with answers such as the following: At the beginning of the tale, Waipuo describes the girl as restless, spoiled, and never satisfied. Waipuo also stresses that the girl has had a sheltered upbringing and is ignorant of the river's danger. With the appearance of the valuable pearl ring, the girl's vivid imagination takes over. Eager to explore faraway, exotic places, she conjures up an underwater kingdom and a romantic young suitor, who she imagines to be a prince. Although she is in love, she feels sorrow and fear on realizing that to be with her beloved she must leave her family. Finally, her impulsive nature leads to her destruction, as she hurries to the river to meet her beloved, and we are led to believe, is swept away.

Difficulty: *Easy*

Objective: *Essay*

17. Students may point out that the tale contains several entertaining elements—for example, an exotic setting, a plot involving mystery and romance, and a tragic ending that leaves the listener with unanswered questions. Some students also may feel that the story includes a central message about the irresistible but potentially dangerous nature of desire.

Difficulty: *Easy*

Objective: *Essay*

Selection Test B, p. 11

Learning About American Stories

1. ANS: C	DIF: Average	OBJ: Literary Analysis
2. ANS: D	DIF: Average	OBJ: Literary Analysis
3. ANS: A	DIF: Average	OBJ: Literary Analysis
4. ANS: C	DIF: Average	OBJ: Literary Analysis
5. ANS: D	DIF: Challenging	OBJ: Literary Analysis
6. ANS: B	DIF: Average	OBJ: Literary Analysis

Critical Reading

7. ANS: B	DIF: Average	OBJ: Comprehension
8. ANS: B	DIF: Challenging	OBJ: Interpretation
9. ANS: B	DIF: Average	OBJ: Comprehension
10. ANS: C	DIF: Average	OBJ: Comprehension
11. ANS: C	DIF: Average	OBJ: Comprehension
12. ANS: B	DIF: Average	OBJ: Interpretation
13. ANS: C	DIF: Average	OBJ: Comprehension
14. ANS: B	DIF: Average	OBJ: Comprehension
15. ANS: C	DIF: Challenging	OBJ: Interpretation
16. ANS: D	DIF: Average	OBJ: Interpretation
17. ANS: A	DIF: Average	OBJ: Comprehension
18. ANS: B	DIF: Challenging	OBJ: Interpretation
19. ANS: A	DIF: Challenging	OBJ: Interpretation
20. ANS: C	DIF: Average	OBJ: Interpretation

Essay

21. Students should point out that both characters expect to get their way or set the agenda. For example, when the granddaughters squabble over who will sit next to Waipuo, the grandmother snaps at them and expects them to listen to her. Later, she abruptly stops answering the girls' questions about her tale and follows her own desire—to go inside. Similarly, Wen Zhiqing's daughter expects her father to listen to her when she insists they continue fishing, and when she escapes to the river, she puts her own desires first. In addition, both characters are revealed as vividly and intensely imaginative, and both possess a mysterious, almost magnetic attraction to the great river. Some students may go so far as to conclude that Waipuo's own fascination with the tale of Wen Zhiqing's daughter stems, at least in part, from identifying with the mysterious girl who was swept away by a flood long ago.

Difficulty: *Average*

Objective: *Essay*

22. Students should point out that the story's remote setting, in both time and place, is likely to appeal to an audience of young listeners. Exotic elements that move the plot forward—for example, the trained cormorants and the pearl ring—would also capture an audience's interest, as would the overall mysterious, romantic plot line involving appealing characters, the beautiful, restless girl and the spirit of the young drowned man. Similarly, the theme of choosing romance and adventure over the familiar is attractive to young people. Students also might mention that Lily's interruptions signal how gripping the grandmother's tale is and that Waipuo's abrupt termination of the storytelling reinforces the tale's suspense and air of mystery.

Difficulty: *Average*

Objective: *Essay*

23. Students may point out that the theme of desire comes up when the girl is described as restless and never satisfied; she longs for adventure and faraway things and places; she vividly imagines that the young man is a prince who has proposed marriage to her. Her desire leads to disaster when she is swept away by the flood. The theme of displacement is evident in the imagery Waipuo uses to suggest the region along the Yangtze River. Specifically, she compares the sound of the prairie crickets to that of the river's water. The author Lan Samantha Chang also describes the farmland of Wisconsin as "*waves* of grass." Students should be able to think of other literary works and films that deal with desire (for example, "Cinderella") and displacement (for example, the myth of Demeter and Persephone), thereby making those themes universal.

Difficulty: *Challenging*

Objective: *Essay*

Unit 6, Part 1 Answers

Diagnostic Test 11, p. 15

MULTIPLE CHOICE

1. ANS: D
2. ANS: C
3. ANS: A
4. ANS: A
5. ANS: B
6. ANS: D
7. ANS: D
8. ANS: C
9. ANS: A
10. ANS: C
11. ANS: B
12. ANS: D
13. ANS: A
14. ANS: A
15. ANS: D

"Why the Waves Have Whitecaps"
by Zora Neale Hurston

Vocabulary Warm-up Exercises, p. 19

A.
1. about
2. the
3. them
4. asked
5. more
6. told
7. I
8. get

B. Sample Answers

1. When I lived close to my elementary school, I *used to* walk there.
2. I would like to baby-sit the younger *children* in my best friend's family.
3. I am *sure* that my best friend likes me because her face always lights up when she sees me at school in the morning.
4. Yes, I strongly agree that *there isn't* ever a good reason, or any reason, to say bad things about people.
5. I *can* relax and be a couch potato every Sunday afternoon.
6. Living in a free country, *we are* certainly the luckiest people in the world.

7. Nothing beats ice water when I need to *quench* my thirst.
8. I have a locket from my grandmother *that's* the most valuable thing I own.

Reading Warm-up A, p. 20

Sample Answers

1. <u>de</u>/the, <u>dird</u>/third, <u>Dursday</u>/Thursday, <u>de</u>/the, <u>dem</u>/them
2. *Ast* means "asked." The passerby *rist* his life trying to pull the driver out of a burning car.
3. <u>po'</u>/poor, <u>mo'</u>/more, <u>talkin'</u>/talking, <u>'bout</u>/about, <u>givin'</u>/giving, <u>'em</u>/them
4. *Ah* ate some *pah* with *ahs* cream on top on the Fourth of *Julah.*
5. *Pen* would be *pin* since the short *i* sound is often used in the dialect.
6. Benji, I have asked you three times to get in the house. Come on now!
7. *Tole* stands for *told.*

Reading Warm-up B, p. 21

Sample Answers

1. Since *ain't* is dialect for *isn't,* the writer has cleverly put them next to each other in the sentence.
2. (we are); *We is* uses incorrect grammar; for example, *we is* unhappy.
3. chilling; *Chillun,* although it sounds like *chilling,* is dialect for *children.*
4. <u>Is that what happens when you close your eyes tightly because you have an itch?</u>; *Squinch* is dialect for *quench.*
5. <u>useter</u>/used to, <u>sho</u>/sure, <u>kin</u>/can, <u>dat's</u>/that's (some students might also list ain't/isn't); I *useter* love to swim laps. However, *dat's* all in the past. I know for *sho* that it's too much work, when I *kin* just float and enjoy myself in the pool instead.

"Why the Waves Have Whitecaps"
by Zora Neale Hurston

Reading: Create a Summary, p. 22

Sample Revision

The wind and the water are both *female* characters. They used to *brag* about their children. ~~Mrs. Wind said one thing and Mrs. Waters said another.~~ Mrs. Water got so sick and tired of hearing about Mrs. Wind's children that one day, when the children came to drink her water, she drowned them. When Mrs. Wind went to look for her children, Mrs. Water said she had not seen them. ~~Mrs. Wind searched high and low.~~ *When* Mrs. Wind passed over the water calling for her children, whitecaps came to the top. *She is still looking— and that is why the waves have whitecaps.*

Literary Analysis: Myth, p. 23

1. It tries to explain why the waves have whitecaps.
2. Annoyed with Mrs. Wind's bragging about her children, Mrs. Water drowns the children when they come to drink. Then, when Mrs. Wind travels over the water seeking her lost children, whitecaps—the feathers of the birds, her children—come to the surface. She is still looking, and that is why the waves have whitecaps.
3. Wind and water are portrayed as mothers.
4. Qualities include pride in one's children, boastfulness, jealousy, vengefulness, violence, maternal love, and sorrow at the death of loved ones.
5. It suggests that nature was important. It shows an interest in a natural phenomenon, whitecaps on waves, and uses other elements of nature to explain it. It shows a familiarity with the ocean.
6. It shows the strength of mother-child relationships; African American dialect; the important role of storytelling; vivid imagination.

Vocabulary Builder, p. 24

A. 1. C; 2. C; 3. A; 4. B; 5. D

B. Sample Answer

"Oh, but I have more different children than anybody else in the world. They fly, they walk, they swim, they sing, they talk, (and) they cry. They have all the colors of the sun. Lord, my children sure are a pleasure. There is no one who has babies like mine."

Enrichment: Ocean Waves, p. 27

1. crest
2. trough
3. wavelength
4. height
5. The waves also would go in different directions.
6. It would bob up and down.
7. It would go up and down with the waves, unless the waves became so big that they swept over the side of the boat, breaking or filling it and sinking it.

Selection Test A, p. 28

Critical Reading

1. ANS: A	DIF: Easy	OBJ: Comprehension
2. ANS: A	DIF: Easy	OBJ: Interpretation
3. ANS: D	DIF: Easy	OBJ: Comprehension
4. ANS: B	DIF: Easy	OBJ: Comprehension
5. ANS: C	DIF: Easy	OBJ: Reading
6. ANS: B	DIF: Easy	OBJ: Reading
7. ANS: C	DIF: Easy	OBJ: Literary Analysis
8. ANS: C	DIF: Easy	OBJ: Literary Analysis

Vocabulary and Grammar

9. ANS: B   DIF: Easy   OBJ: Vocabulary
10. ANS: B   DIF: Easy   OBJ: Grammar

Essay

11. Students should recognize that the myth explains why the waves have whitecaps. Students should itemize the main events of the plot that lead to this situation: Mrs. Wind and Mrs. Water brag about their children; Mrs. Wind brags so much that Mrs. Water grows to hate Mrs. Wind's children and drowns them when they come for a drink; and whitecaps form because Mrs. Wind is passing over the water, searching for her children.
    Difficulty: *Easy*
    Objective: *Essay*

Selection Test B, p. 30

Critical Reading

1. ANS: A   DIF: Average   OBJ: Interpretation
2. ANS: A   DIF: Average   OBJ: Interpretation
3. ANS: C   DIF: Challenging   OBJ: Interpretation
4. ANS: C   DIF: Average   OBJ: Reading
5. ANS: C   DIF: Average   OBJ: Comprehension
6. ANS: B   DIF: Average   OBJ: Interpretation
7. ANS: A   DIF: Average   OBJ: Reading
8. ANS: A   DIF: Challenging   OBJ: Literary Analysis
9. ANS: D   DIF: Average   OBJ: Literary Analysis

Vocabulary and Grammar

10. ANS: A   DIF: Average   OBJ: Vocabulary
11. ANS: C   DIF: Average   OBJ: Grammar

Essay

12. Students should recognize that both women are proud of their children; brag about them, as proud parents often do; and grow competitive in their bragging. Further, they should recognize the humanness in Mrs. Wind when she is upset over the loss of her children and searches for them. Students should recognize that the two women, since they are actually forces of nature, have an unrealistically large number of children and that the action Mrs. Water takes in her annoyance—drowning Mrs. Wind's children—is far more drastic than is typical of everyday human beings engaged in a bragging contest.
    Difficulty: *Average*
    Objective: *Essay*

13. Students should recognize that a myth is an old tale that presents the beliefs or customs of the culture that produces it. They might note that a myth usually

explains events in nature or in a people's history and that a myth often describes the actions of supernatural creatures, animal characters, or natural forces as if they were human. Students should then explain how this myth illustrates those qualities—presenting the old African American explanation of whitecaps and featuring natural forces that display human traits.
Difficulty: *Challenging*
Objective: *Essay*

"Coyote Steals the Sun and Moon"
retold by Richard Erdoes and Alfonso Ortiz

Vocabulary Warm-up Exercises, p. 33

A. 1. chattering
2. coyote
3. curiosity
4. panting
5. lend
6. produce
7. eagle
8. nudged

B. Sample Answers

1. F; People would not be able to peel the thick skin of *squashes* with their fingers.
2. F; A *pueblo* would not be found in Maine in the Northeast, but in the southwestern states.
3. F; If the school buses are *delayed*, the students will be late to school.
4. T; When rainfall has *lagged* behind usual levels, there is probably not enough water, resulting in plants that have *shriveled*.
5. F; People would welcome napkins when eating juicy *melons*.
6. T; A neighbor's dog constantly barking could certainly be described as *pestering*.
7. F; A *sacred* promise is a very serious vow you can make and more important than a passing remark.

Reading Warm-up A, p. 34

Sample Answers

1. At least, I would interrupt nearly every sentence to ask questions; My *curiosity* about the stars has been present in me since I was a small child.
2. (to get her attention); My sister *nudged* me a little too hard with her elbow, and I yelled out in pain.
3. (a story); *Produce* means "to make something happen."
4. by the time the it [the story] ended; Breathing fast is one response to feeling excited, so you could find yourself *panting*.
5. (magnificent, sly); An *eagle* is powerful, and a *coyote* is tricky.

6. <u>Mom's stories</u>; *Lend* means "to let someone borrow something for a short time."

7. (public speaking); My teeth have been *chattering* when I've been scared, when I've been cold, and when I've been sick with the flu.

Reading Warm-up B, p. 35

Sample Answers

1. <u>nature</u>; One thing that is *sacred* to me is the quilt that my great grandmother made and that has been in our family for a very long time.

2. (animals, bugs); Bugs probably kept up their *pestering* by biting people or buzzing around their heads.

3. (villages); A *pueblo* was a bunch of homes that were connected together and made from dried mud or clay mixed with sticks.

4. <u>you might not get back in</u>; *Lagged* means "moved more slowly than others."

5. (No one); I was *delayed* in getting to my music lesson last weekend when the bus came really late.

6. (corn, beans); *Squashes* are vegetables and *melons* are fruits, but they both have thick skins.

7. <u>died</u>; *Shriveled* means "dried up and withered."

"Coyote Steals the Sun and Moon"
retold by Richard Erdoes and Alfonso Ortiz

Reading: Create a Summary, p. 36

A. 1. Coyote, Eagle

2. a river; the pueblo; a hill; the sky or a distant part of the sky, where the sun and moon run

3. Coyote's request that he and Eagle hunt together; Coyote's complaint about lack of light; Coyote's insistence on carrying the box; Eagle's demand that Coyote not look inside

4. Coyote and Eagle team up to hunt; they search for light; they visit the pueblo, where the Kachinas dance; they steal the box with the sun and moon; Coyote obtains the box; he disobeys Eagle and looks inside; as a result, the sun and the moon are far away for portions of the year, and winter comes.

B. **Sample Answer**

To get more food, Coyote persuades Eagle, a better hunter, to hunt with him. Coyote then convinces Eagle that they need more light so that Coyote can hunt better. The two go to a pueblo in search of light and find the sun and the moon in two boxes. Coyote wants to steal the boxes, while Eagle prefers just to borrow them, but Coyote prevails. After Coyote nags, Eagle lets him carry the box (in which he combines the sun and the moon). When Coyote then disobeys Eagle and looks inside, the moon and the sun fly off to a distant part of the sky. And that is why we have winter cold for a part of each year.

Literary Analysis: Myth, p. 37

2. Southwestern Native American villages are called pueblos; the Zuñi live in villages called pueblos.

3. Kachinas are an important part of Zuñi religious beliefs and practices.

4. Native Americans like the Zuñi have chiefs, or tribal leaders.

5. It is a Zuñi custom to give someone something if he asks for it four times.

6. Southwestern Native Americans grow peaches, squashes, and melons.

Vocabulary Builder, p. 38

A. **Samples Answers**

1. The Bible is one book that many people consider *sacred*.

2. Raisins are small *shriveled* fruit made by drying grapes in the sun.

3. A police car uses its siren when in *pursuit* of a criminal.

4. Most people get upset by constant *pestering*.

B. 1. C; 2. A; 3. D; 4. B

Enrichment: Coyote the Trickster, p. 41

A. 1. People enjoy reading about clever and unusual behavior.

2. Coyotes are clever, adaptable animals that sometimes get the better of human beings.

B. Accept all reasonable responses that students defend effectively.

"Why the Waves Have Whitecaps"
by Zora Neale Hurston

"Coyote Steals the Sun and the Moon"
retold by Richard Erdoes and Alfonso Ortiz

Build Language Skills: Vocabulary, p. 42

A. Sample Answers

1. Janis shook her head to show that she *dis*agreed.

2. The director was *dis*pleased with the poor performances.

3. The ferry is *dis*continuing operation, so you cannot take it next month.

4. She *dis*mounted from the horse and led it to the barn.

5. The people booed and hissed *dis*respectfully when the king passed.

B. 1. organized; 2. essential; 3. sequence;

4. disorganized; 5. extract

Build Language Skills: Grammar, p. 43

Sentence Structures

A. 1. compound: <u>The Northwest is damp and rainy</u>, but <u>the Southwest is dry</u>.

2. complex: <u>When it rains</u>, <u>many desert flowers bloom</u>.

B. Sample Answers

1. The beach traffic is usually heavy in summer, but this weekend was an exception.
2. As I stood on the beach, the waves rushed to shore, and the seagulls flew overhead.

"Coyote Steals the Sun and Moon"
retold by Richard Erdoes and Alfonso Ortiz

Selection Test A, p. 44

Critical Reading

1. ANS: A	DIF: Easy	OBJ: Comprehension
2. ANS: B	DIF: Easy	OBJ: Comprehension
3. ANS: A	DIF: Easy	OBJ: Interpretation
4. ANS: D	DIF: Easy	OBJ: Comprehension
5. ANS: D	DIF: Easy	OBJ: Interpretation
6. ANS: A	DIF: Easy	OBJ: Comprehension
7. ANS: A	DIF: Easy	OBJ: Reading
8. ANS: B	DIF: Easy	OBJ: Reading
9. ANS: B	DIF: Easy	OBJ: Interpretation
10. ANS: C	DIF: Easy	OBJ: Literary Analysis
11. ANS: D	DIF: Easy	OBJ: Literary Analysis
12. ANS: A	DIF: Easy	OBJ: Literary Analysis

Vocabulary and Grammar

13. ANS: B	DIF: Easy	OBJ: Vocabulary
14. ANS: D	DIF: Easy	OBJ: Grammar
15. ANS: A	DIF: Easy	OBJ: Vocabulary

Essay

16. Students should recognize that the myth explains how the sun and moon came to be in the sky, which is one of the reasons we have cold and winter, not year-round summer. Students should itemize the main events of the plot that lead to this situation: Coyote persuades Eagle to hunt with him, Coyote says he needs light to hunt, the two visit the pueblo and steal the box of light, Coyote persuades Eagle to let him carry the box, Coyote opens the box even though he is not supposed to, and the sun and moon escape into the sky.

    Difficulty: *Easy*
    Objective: *Essay*

17. Students should recognize that Coyote is clever, dishonest, mischievous, curious, persuasive, and/or self-important. They should cite examples of his behavior to illustrate each quality they name. For instance, he shows cleverness in getting Eagle to hunt with him, dishonesty in blaming his poor hunting skills on lack of light, his

mischievous side and curiosity in opening the box, persuasion in making Eagle hunt with him and steal the box, and self-importance in demanding to hold the box.

Difficulty: *Easy*
Objective: *Essay*

Selection Test B, p. 47

Critical Reading

1. ANS: A	DIF: Average	OBJ: Comprehension
2. ANS: A	DIF: Average	OBJ: Interpretation
3. ANS: C	DIF: Average	OBJ: Literary Analysis
4. ANS: C	DIF: Average	OBJ: Reading
5. ANS: B	DIF: Average	OBJ: Comprehension
6. ANS: C	DIF: Average	OBJ: Interpretation
7. ANS: D	DIF: Average	OBJ: Interpretation
8. ANS: D	DIF: Average	OBJ: Interpretation
9. ANS: A	DIF: Average	OBJ: Reading
10. ANS: C	DIF: Challenging	OBJ: Literary Analysis
11. ANS: B	DIF: Average	OBJ: Literary Analysis
12. ANS: C	DIF: Challenging	OBJ: Literary Analysis
13. ANS: C	DIF: Average	OBJ: Literary Analysis

Vocabulary and Grammar

14. ANS: D	DIF: Average	OBJ: Vocabulary
15. ANS: A	DIF: Average	OBJ: Vocabulary
16. ANS: B	DIF: Average	OBJ: Grammar
17. ANS: C	DIF: Average	OBJ: Grammar

Essay

18. Students may say that the myth teaches the danger of curiosity or the danger of letting someone persuade you to do something that you know is wrong. If students choose to write about the first danger, they should provide events and details that show how calamity befalls Coyote, Eagle, and the whole world. If students choose to write about changing one's values to suit someone else, they should discuss how Eagle was persuaded to steal the box when he at first did not wish to.

    Difficulty: *Average*
    Objective: *Essay*

19. Students should recognize that Coyote is more clever, tricky, mischievous, and curious than Eagle, and that Eagle is more honest and gullible and less knowledgeable than Coyote, but also more skilled as a hunter. They should cite examples from the myth to illustrate the points they make about the characters—for example, Eagle expects Coyote to fly and does not understand why Coyote cannot, or Eagle does not need to peek in

the box the way Coyote does. In discussing their inter-
action, students should consider how Coyote persuades
Eagle to hunt together and to steal the box of light; they
also should consider how Coyote's pestering eventually
persuades Eagle to give Coyote the box, against his better judgment.

Difficulty: *Average*

Objective: *Essay*

"Chicoria" adapted by José Griego y Maestas, retold by Rudolfo A. Anaya

from *"The People, Yes"* by Carl Sandburg

Vocabulary Warm-up Exercises, p. 51

A.
1. poets
2. yarns
3. recited
4. accord
5. spinning
6. shame
7. cyclone
8. straddling

B. Sample Answers

1. We saw cars *whizzing* along on the highway at 70 miles an hour.
2. We *boasted* that we could *compete* with all other soccer teams.
3. We *predicted* that we would be late, and *furthermore* that we would be tired.
4. During the drought, we could walk right in the *riverbed.*
5. The master *instructed* his servants to do everything he told them.
6. In *weaving* a twisty tale of suspense, the director used lots of scary effects.

Reading Warm-up A, p. 52

Sample Answers

1. (tall tales); One of my favorite *yarns* is the story of how the rabbit got long ears.
2. (tell); *Spinning* means "telling stories that you have invented."
3. verses; One of my favorite *poets* is Ogden Nash.
4. (rode); Someone *straddling* a *cyclone* might be sitting on top of a huge funnel cloud with his or her legs dangling on both sides, and holding on for dear life.
5. decides; Something I did on my own *accord* was donate my allowance to the disaster victims.
6. dies wearing himself out; Of course, there is no *embarrassment* in that!
7. many of the stories about his feats; I *recited* the Pledge of Allegiance.

Reading Warm-up B, p. 53

Sample Answers

1. (bragging); When I got my new bike, I *boasted* that it was the best one on the block.
2. command; My grandma *instructed* me to walk the dog.
3. (further, more); I'm not going on the ski trip because I don't know how to ski. *Furthermore*, I hate cold weather.
4. contest; I like to *compete* in swim meets.
5. (great things for me [Angel]); I *predicted* that my sister would be elected president of her class, and I was right.
6. (stones); I have watched the Blue Angels go *whizzing* by tall buildings.
7. (dry); Water cannot flow on a dry *riverbed* because the *riverbed* is the ground at the bottom of a body of water such as a river.
8. He [Angel]; I would go about *weaving* jokes into my talk by first giving some information and then telling a joke. Then, I'd go back to giving some facts, and in while, tell another joke.

"Chicoria" adapted by José Griego y Maestas, retold by Rudolfo A. Anaya

from *The People, Yes* by Carl Sandburg

Reading: Use a Graphic to Summarize Literature, p. 54

Students should create a time line, a cluster diagram, or
any other graphic aid that organizes the main ideas or
events of the selection.

Sample Answers

They have yarns

Of a poor poet from New Mexico who, before facing off with a
California poet, used tall tales to win himself a seat at a rich
rancher's banquet table.

Literary Analysis: Oral Tradition, p. 55

Sample Answers

Yarn: Pecos Pete; *Exaggerated Detail:* straddling cyclone;
Factual Detail: cyclones in Texas

Yarn: man driving bees; *Exaggerated Detail:* driving bees
over Rocky Mountains; *Factual Detail:* Rocky Mountains are
next to a desert

Yarn: ship's captain; *Exaggerated Detail:* shadow frozen to
deck; *Factual Details:* cold on ships, mutinies on some
ships, tedious duties on ships

Yarn: cyclone; *Exaggerated Details:* sucked objects up chimney flue, picked up wagontracks in Nebraska and dropped
them in Dakota; *Factual Details:* cyclones lift objects, carry
them great distances, and drop them in odd places

Yarn: herd of cattle; *Exaggerated Detail:* cattle getting lost
in redwood tree; *Factual Details:* California has very large
redwoods

Vocabulary Builder, p. 56

A. 1. T; 2. F; 3. F

B. Sample Answers

1. Yes, the queen acts *haughty* in some fairy tales.
2. Yes, a *cyclone* could destroy a farmer's crops.
3. Yes, a good receptionist usually greets visitors *cordially*.

C. 1. D; 2. A; 3. D

Enrichment: How Jobs Change, p. 59

A. Sample Answers

2. line 4, farmer: plants and sows crops
3. line 10, beekeeper: raises bees and sells the honey
4. line 11, railroad engineer: operates a train
5. line 11, railroad conductor: collects tickets from train passengers and assists them
6. line 15, ship's captain: commands ship

B. Sample Answer

Job affected by technology: farming

1. The poem implies that farming is difficult because the farmer can control neither the way the crop develops nor the effects of weather on the crop.
2. Farm size has grown, with small farms increasingly giving way to larger ones, and the cost of running a farm also has increased. Farmers now have access to computer programs that can help them plan land use and sell crops more effectively, satellites provide better weather forecasts, and headlights make it easier to operate machinery. However, farming still remains a risky business, and the weather is still impossible to control.

Selection Test A, p. 60

Critical Reading

1. ANS: C	DIF: Easy	OBJ: Comprehension
2. ANS: B	DIF: Easy	OBJ: Comprehension
3. ANS: A	DIF: Easy	OBJ: Interpretation
4. ANS: B	DIF: Easy	OBJ: Interpretation
5. ANS: B	DIF: Easy	OBJ: Reading
6. ANS: C	DIF: Easy	OBJ: Literary Analysis
7. ANS: D	DIF: Easy	OBJ: Literary Analysis
8. ANS: D	DIF: Easy	OBJ: Reading
9. ANS: B	DIF: Easy	OBJ: Comprehension
10. ANS: D	DIF: Easy	OBJ: Interpretation
11. ANS: C	DIF: Easy	OBJ: Interpretation
12. ANS: D	DIF: Easy	OBJ: Literary Analysis

Vocabulary and Grammar

13. ANS: D	DIF: Easy	OBJ: Vocabulary
14. ANS: A	DIF: Easy	OBJ: Vocabulary
15. ANS: B	DIF: Easy	OBJ: Grammar

Essay

16. Students should explain the reason Chicoria comes to California, his expectations regarding the rancher's dinner, the bet he makes with the servant, and the stories he tells to win the bet. Chicoria teaches that someone who can feed others shouldn't leave someone out just because he is not of the same economic class.

Difficulty: *Easy*

Objective: *Essay*

17. Students should choose any two of the summarized yarns, accurately restate them, and correctly pinpoint the exaggerated detail or details they contain. For instance, they might say, "One man had whiskers so long that if the wind blew the right way the whiskers would get to the man's destination a day before him. The exaggerated detail is the length of the man's whiskers."

Difficulty: *Easy*

Objective: *Essay*

Selection Test B, p. 63

Critical Reading

1. ANS: B	DIF: Average	OBJ: Comprehension
2. ANS: A	DIF: Average	OBJ: Interpretation
3. ANS: D	DIF: Average	OBJ: Reading
4. ANS: D	DIF: Average	OBJ: Literary Analysis
5. ANS: A	DIF: Average	OBJ: Literary Analysis
6. ANS: D	DIF: Challenging	OBJ: Literary Analysis
7. ANS: A	DIF: Average	OBJ: Reading
8. ANS: A	DIF: Average	OBJ: Literary Analysis
9. ANS: D	DIF: Challenging	OBJ: Comprehension
10. ANS: A	DIF: Average	OBJ: Interpretation
11. ANS: A	DIF: Challenging	OBJ: Literary Analysis
12. ANS: A	DIF: Average	OBJ: Literary Analysis

Vocabulary and Grammar

13. ANS: B	DIF: Average	OBJ: Vocabulary
14. ANS: C	DIF: Average	OBJ: Vocabulary
15. ANS: A	DIF: Average	OBJ: Vocabulary
16. ANS: C	DIF: Average	OBJ: Grammar
17. ANS: C	DIF: Average	OBJ: Grammar

Essay

18. Essays should recognize that Chicoria is talented at both poetry and storytelling. They should focus on how skill at poetry gains Chicoria a degree of respect and how his ability to tell stories gains him even more respect when he uses those stories to shame the rancher and teach him an important lesson.

Difficulty: *Average*

Objective: *Essay*

19. Students should recognize that many of the yarns deal with farming or ranching and boats and trains, suggesting the dominance of those occupations and those modes of transportation. Students should recognize that the many details about weather disasters such as cyclones bespeak a world where more Americans lived closer to danger and faced climatic danger more regularly than they do today. They should also recognize how the stories people told show a delight in unusual events, exaggeration, and humor.

Difficulty: *Average*
Objective: *Essay*

"Brer Possum's Dilemma" by Jackie Torrence
"John Henry" Traditional

Vocabulary Warm-up Exercises, p. 67

A. 1. You's
2. Brer
3. critters
4. a-doin'
5. outa
6. offa

B. Sample Answers
1. Jim is the name of a *feller* who's a hero in my life.
2. I *reckon* summer vacation will be very busy.
3. I'm telling you *agin* that the radius of a circle is half the distance across it.
4. I'm always careful when I cross the street *'cause* the traffic is heavy.
5. I think I'll mind growing *ol'* because I probably won't be able to play soccer then.
6. If I had a male dog, I'd call *'im* Duke.

Reading Warm-up A, p. 68

Sample Answers
1. (brother); *Brer* Fox thought he was as clever as *Brer* Rabbit.
2. creatures; Some of the *critters* in the folk tales were a rabbit, a fox, a wolf, and a bear. (Possum, snake, and turtle were also mentioned.)
3. (you are); *We's* going now.
4. doing; I'm *a-hopin'* to see you tomorrow.
5. (out of), (off of), *fulla*; I'm *fulla* good ideas today.

Reading Warm-up B, p. 69

Sample Answers
1. (Ol' Brer Rabbit), (ol' Brer Fox); The writer probably uses the word *ol'* to make it sound like he knows the characters. Using *ol'* makes the story seem friendly.
2. (Brer Rabbit); It looks as if she's a goner, but then she tricks ol' Brer Fox into freeing *'er.*

3. (Brer Rabbit always gets away); *Once again,* he gets the better of Brer Fox, even though he's smaller and weaker.
4. (reckon) I *reckon* that I can get a good grade on the test if I study hard enough.
5. ('cause, feller); I think that you do have to know what you are doing and be clever *because* sometimes the other *fellow* will try to outsmart you.

"Brer Possum's Dilemma" by Jackie Torrence
"John Henry" Traditional

Reading: Use a Graphic to Summarize Literature, p. 70

Students should create a time line, a cluster diagram, or any other graphic aid that organizes the main ideas or events of the selection.

Sample Answer

When Brer Snake asks for help in removing the brick on his back and getting out of a hole, Brer Possum wants to help but also knows that the snake is likely to bite him. In both cases, Brer Possum finds a way to help from a distance. When Brer Snake then says how cold he is and asks to be put in Brer Possum's pocket for warmth, Brer Possum is again reluctant but finally agrees to do it, whereupon Brer Snake bites him.

Literary Analysis: Oral Tradition, p. 71

A. 1. B; 2. C; 3. A; 4. D
B. Students who find the dialect effective may say that it gives the selections an oral quality that makes them seem more folksy and authentic. Those who do not find the dialect effective may feel it makes little difference, or they may find the dialect awkward, hard to understand, or unevenly executed.

Vocabulary Builder, p. 72

A. 1. T; 2. F
B. Sample Answers
1. A motherless kitten is a *pitiful* sight.
2. Some say the twenty-first century *commenced* in 2000; some say in 2001.
C. 1. D; 2. A

Enrichment: John Henry and Technological Change, p. 75

Sample Answers
1. A. Before the Civil War, most African Americans were slaves.
   B. Some students may feel that John Henry's life as a slave helps explain his desire to prove himself or may make his achievements in life even more heroic.
2. Chesapeake and Ohio

3. A. They probably resented the drills because the drills would replace them and they would no longer have their job.
   B. John Henry challenges the drill because he resents it and wants to prove that automation will never be as good as a human being.
4. Among other things, John Henry rose from humble beginnings to perform a remarkable feat, he was remarkable in appearance in his day, and his victory over the drill made workers who resented new machinery feel better about themselves and their work efforts.

"Chicoria" adapted by José Griego y Maestas, retold by Rudolfo A. Anaya
from *The People, Yes* by Carl Sandburg
"Brer Possum's Dilemma" by Jackie Torrence
"John Henry" Traditional

Build Language Skills: Vocabulary, p. 76

The prefix *un-*

A. Sample Answers

1. *Unlock* the door when you enter the house.
2. He had a cold, *unfriendly* sneer.
3. She studied very little and was *unprepared* for the test.
4. Junk food is *unnecessary* food in most diets.
5. You need to *unfold* the letter to remove it from an envelope.

B. 1. I; *sample sentence:* Put the numbers in the right *sequence*.
2. C
3. I; *sample sentence:* The piano player kept the sheets of music *organized*.
4. I; *sample sentence:* A bathing cap is *essential* in some pools.

Build Language Skills: Grammar, p. 77

Commas

A. 1. When I read, I prefer humorous yarns.
2. Annie Oakley, a famous sharpshooter, appeared in one tale that I read.
3. I also read folk tales about Brer Possum, Paul Bunyan, and Pecos Bill.

B. Sample Answers

1. People enjoy all kinds of music, but not everyone likes the same kind.
2. I like the singers Nanci Griffith, Amy Grant, and Natalie Merchant.
3. When I first heard it, I thought that song was beautiful.
4. Those lyrics are in dialect, the language and grammar of a particular region or people.

"Brer Possum's Dilemma" by Jackie Torrence
"John Henry" Traditional

Selection Test A, p. 78

Critical Reading

1. ANS: A	DIF: Easy	OBJ: Interpretation
2. ANS: D	DIF: Easy	OBJ: Comprehension
3. ANS: A	DIF: Easy	OBJ: Interpretation
4. ANS: D	DIF: Easy	OBJ: Interpretation
5. ANS: C	DIF: Easy	OBJ: Reading
6. ANS: B	DIF: Easy	OBJ: Literary Analysis
7. ANS: A	DIF: Easy	OBJ: Comprehension
8. ANS: A	DIF: Easy	OBJ: Literary Analysis
9. ANS: C	DIF: Easy	OBJ: Comprehension
10. ANS: C	DIF: Easy	OBJ: Interpretation
11. ANS: C	DIF: Easy	OBJ: Reading
12. ANS: D	DIF: Easy	OBJ: Literary Analysis

Vocabulary and Grammar

13. ANS: D	DIF: Easy	OBJ: Vocabulary
14. ANS: A	DIF: Easy	OBJ: Vocabulary
15. ANS: B	DIF: Easy	OBJ: Grammar

Essay

16. Students' summaries should mention the three requests Brer Snake makes, Brer Possum's reluctance to put himself in likely danger but his desire to help, and Brer Snake's ultimate betrayal. Students should recognize that the possum is supposed to learn about the danger of putting yourself in harm's way—that is, in the power of someone likely to harm you.

Difficulty: *Easy*

Objective: *Essay*

17. Students should recognize that John Henry was a very large man for his day, probably African American, strong, determined, hard working, skilled, and proud of his work. They should cite details from the selection to support the statements they make about John Henry. Some students may discuss the wisdom of John Henry's drive, which cost him his life.

Difficulty: *Easy*

Objective: *Essay*

Selection Test B, p. 81

Critical Reading

1. ANS: D	DIF: Average	OBJ: Comprehension
2. ANS: C	DIF: Challenging	OBJ: Interpretation
3. ANS: B	DIF: Average	OBJ: Interpretation
4. ANS: C	DIF: Average	OBJ: Reading

5. ANS: A	DIF: Average	OBJ: Interpretation
6. ANS: D	DIF: Challenging	OBJ: Literary Analysis
7. ANS: D	DIF: Challenging	OBJ: Literary Analysis
8. ANS: A	DIF: Average	OBJ: Comprehension
9. ANS: D	DIF: Average	OBJ: Interpretation
10. ANS: B	DIF: Average	OBJ: Reading
11. ANS: A	DIF: Average	OBJ: Interpretation
12. ANS: A	DIF: Average	OBJ: Interpretation
13. ANS: A	DIF: Average	OBJ: Literary Analysis

Vocabulary and Grammar

14. ANS: D	DIF: Average	OBJ: Vocabulary
15. ANS: A	DIF: Average	OBJ: Vocabulary
16. ANS: C	DIF: Average	OBJ: Grammar
17. ANS: C	DIF: Average	OBJ: Grammar

Essay

18. Sample answers: It is dangerous to be kind to potential enemies if your kindness gives them strength or power over you. Do not expect others to change their nature simply because you treat them well. Don't go looking for trouble. Regardless of which theme students mention, they should show how the events of the story—Brer Possum's wary kindness and unwise decision to put the snake in his pocket—lead to a bad end for that character. Students who focus on the second theme should also include Brer Snake's remark, "You knowed I was a snake before you put me in your pocket."

Difficulty: *Average*

Objective: *Essay*

19. Students should recount the main events of the tale in paragraph form: the baby John Henry's prediction; the arrival of the steam drill and John Henry's challenge of it; the injury; the death; the funeral and aftermath. Retellings should include details where appropriate—for example, some of the dialogue and dialect.

Difficulty: *Average*

Objective: *Essay*

"Western Wagons" by Stephen Vincent Benét
"Davy Crockett's Dream" by Davy Crockett
"Paul Bunyan of the North Woods"
by Carl Sandburg

Vocabulary Warm-up Exercises, p. 85

A. 1. youngster
2. blaze
3. mocking
4. reformed
5. kindled

6. revenge
7. amid
8. bellowing

B. Sample Answers

1. It was the hare's bad *fortune* to lose the race to the tortoise.
2. The *whirlwind* traveled north up the middle of the *continent*.
3. We needed a lot of trucks to carry the *legions* of soldiers to the waiting ship.
4. Touching a hot *griddle* is unwise and could hurt you more than a *trifle*.
5. By accident, the carpenter *gouged* a deep hole in the beautiful table he had built.
6. The *squatter* did not want the police to know his new address.

Reading Warm-up A, p. 86

Sample Answers

1. (himself); Unfortunately, I could hear the nasty kids *mocking* Dmitri's foreign accent.
2. loudmouth, heard; The elephant in the zoo was *bellowing* so loudly that it scared our baby sister.
3. a trail through the mountains to what is now Tennessee; *Blazed* means "made or marked, as a trail."
4. (Growing up); When you're a *youngster*, you can swing on tire attached to a tree.
5. (many a fire); When we went camping, we *kindled* a large fire so that we could roast marshmallows.
6. (some of his wilder ways); People with bad habits can become *reformed* by giving up those habits.
7. sent its army to claim the land; In *Star Wars*, the Jedi took *revenge* on the evil empire.
8. 2,000 Mexicans; When the battle was over, 187 Americans lay dead *among* the 2,000 Mexican soldiers they had killed.

Reading Warm-up B, p. 87

Sample Answers

1. (blow into Hooten Hollow, stir things up, and blow out again just as fast); The wind would probably be so intense that a real *whirlwind* would knock me off my feet.
2. (paid for it); A *squatter* might live in an abandoned warehouse.
3. California; The story takes place on the *continent* of North America.
4. holes in the ground Jarvis *gouged* out a section of the wall and hid his money in it.
5. (thousands); There would be *legions* of soldiers on a battlefield.
6. (twelve white horses); An ordinary *griddle* is usually no more than 12 square inches.

7. They saw the big effort she was making with all those animals and supplies, and they knew she wanted to win more than a trifle, or just a little bit. I want to be a successful actor more than a *trifle*.

8. (Wanda whipped up 1,212 flapjacks); I have the *good fortune* of being in excellent health.

"Western Wagons" by Stephen Vincent Benét
"Davy Crockett's Dream" by Davy Crockett
"Paul Bunyan of the North Woods"
by Carl Sandburg

Literary Analysis: Comparing Heroic Characters, p. 88

Sample Answers

1. Pioneers in "Western Wagons" headed west to unknown lands knowing only that they would encounter hardships (starving, freezing, or dying); Crockett went hunting on an extremely cold day; Bunyan drove oxen across the frozen ocean, swam up a pillar of rain.

2. Pioneers in "Western Wagons" overcame challenges by breaking and clearing land; Crockett overcame a challenge by changing tack: not finding anything to hunt in the freezing cold, he went inside an abandoned hut, built a fire, and took a nap; after it had rained for too long, Bunyan turned off the rain; he also drowned bee mosquitoes that ate one of his oxen.

3. Actions of pioneers in "Western Wagons" do not seem exaggerated; exaggeration about Crockett includes his hat freezing to his head, icicles crackling inside his nose with a sneeze, taking a nap on chestnut burs with head looking up the fireplace, entire dream, long icicle on wife's nose jabbing him in the eye; exaggerations about Bunyan include driving a team of oxen across the ocean, Seven Axmen and Bunyan dancing on a floor two hundred feet down, turning off the rain, two mosquitoes eating an ox and mating with bees, a cook stove covering an acre and a table three miles long, Benny growing out of his barn in one night and eating a stove.

4. Pioneers in "Western Wagons" are real historical figures; Crockett is a combination of real historical figure and fictional legend; Bunyan is a fictional legend.

Vocabulary Builder, p. 89

A. Sample Answers

1. No, campers want to put out their fires, not start them, before they leave a campsite.

2. No, young executives would not want to live in roughly built cabins or shacks, which they would consider beneath their means.

3. No, I would not have trouble hearing someone who is roaring at me.

4. No, squatters are people illegally on land and would not want the police or government to know where they are living.

5. While watching a movie, most prefer the people in front of them to sit still rather than make noisy movements.

B. 1. B; 2. D; 3. C; 4. A

Selection Test A, p. 91
Critical Reading

1. ANS: B	DIF: Easy	OBJ: Comprehension
2. ANS: D	DIF: Easy	OBJ: Interpretation
3. ANS: B	DIF: Easy	OBJ: Literary Analysis
4. ANS: C	DIF: Easy	OBJ: Literary Analysis
5. ANS: C	DIF: Easy	OBJ: Comprehension
6. ANS: A	DIF: Easy	OBJ: Comprehension
7. ANS: D	DIF: Easy	OBJ: Interpretation
8. ANS: A	DIF: Easy	OBJ: Literary Analysis
9. ANS: D	DIF: Easy	OBJ: Comprehension
10. ANS: B	DIF: Easy	OBJ: Interpretation
11. ANS: C	DIF: Easy	OBJ: Literary Analysis
12. ANS: D	DIF: Easy	OBJ: Literary Analysis

Vocabulary

13. ANS: B	DIF: Easy	OBJ: Vocabulary
14. ANS: A	DIF: Easy	OBJ: Vocabulary
15. ANS: D	DIF: Easy	OBJ: Vocabulary

Essay

16. The characters in all three selections are heroic because they are pioneers of the western frontier. In "Western Wagons," the pioneers risk starvation and death to move west. They overcome difficult circumstances by moving on and taming the land. In "Davy Crockett's Dream," Crockett shows courage by living in the wilderness and going out hunting for food when the weather is freezing. He overcomes the weather—if not the hunting problem—by taking a nap somewhere warmer. Paul Bunyan has great strength and is very clever. He overcomes difficult circumstances like too much rain or ox-eating mosquitoes by using his mind and his strength. Students will have differing opinions as to which character is the most heroic, but they should explain their opinion.

Difficulty: *Easy*

Objective: *Essay*

17. There is no obvious exaggeration in "Western Wagons," and the tone of the poem is serious and admiring. Exaggerations in the Crockett piece include Crockett's hat freezing to his head and his belch turning into a whirlwind up the chimney. Exaggerations in the Bunyan piece include swimming up a pillar of water to turn off the rain and drowning big bee mosquitoes. The tone in

the Crockett piece is humorous and even makes fun of
Crockett himself. The tone in the Bunyan piece is also
humorous, while at the same time admiring of the hero.

Difficulty: *Easy*

Objective: *Essay*

Selection Test B, p. 94

Critical Reading

1. **ANS:** B	**DIF:** Average	**OBJ:** Comprehension
2. **ANS:** D	**DIF:** Average	**OBJ:** Interpretation
3. **ANS:** D	**DIF:** Challenging	**OBJ:** Interpretation
4. **ANS:** C	**DIF:** Challenging	**OBJ:** Interpretation
5. **ANS:** C	**DIF:** Average	**OBJ:** Literary Analysis
6. **ANS:** D	**DIF:** Average	**OBJ:** Literary Analysis
7. **ANS:** A	**DIF:** Challenging	**OBJ:** Interpretation
8. **ANS:** B	**DIF:** Average	**OBJ:** Comprehension
9. **ANS:** C	**DIF:** Average	**OBJ:** Comprehension
10. **ANS:** A	**DIF:** Average	**OBJ:** Literary Analysis
11. **ANS:** A	**DIF:** Challenging	**OBJ:** Literary Analysis
12. **ANS:** A	**DIF:** Challenging	**OBJ:** Interpretation
13. **ANS:** D	**DIF:** Average	**OBJ:** Comprehension
14. **ANS:** B	**DIF:** Average	**OBJ:** Comprehension
15. **ANS:** A	**DIF:** Average	**OBJ:** Literary Analysis
16. **ANS:** D	**DIF:** Average	**OBJ:** Literary Analysis

Vocabulary

17. **ANS:** B	**DIF:** Average	**OBJ:** Vocabulary
18. **ANS:** D	**DIF:** Average	**OBJ:** Vocabulary
19. **ANS:** A	**DIF:** Average	**OBJ:** Vocabulary
20. **ANS:** C	**DIF:** Average	**OBJ:** Vocabulary

Essay

21. Both characters are strong and exaggerated. However,
Crockett is heroic only by virtue of going out to hunt in
the freezing cold. He doesn't seem very heroic when he
escapes the freezing cold by going into an abandoned
cabin, building a fire, and taking a nap. Rather, the
exaggeration associated with Crockett hinges on the
outlandish things that happen to him—such as his hat
freezing to his head and his belching turning into a
whirlwind up the chimney. Davy Crockett is an actual
historical figure who became a legend.

Bunyan's actions are heroic—for example, stopping the
rain by swimming up a pillar of water and getting rid of
ferocious bee mosquitoes. He and the other characters
in the story are exaggerated throughout. He drives a
team of oxen over the frozen Pacific Ocean and so on.
Paul Bunyan is a fictional legend.

Difficulty: *Average*

Objective: *Essay*

22. In "Western Wagons," the pioneers are portrayed as courageous and determined people. They face starvation,
freezing, suffering, and death and they still choose to
go. They succeed in moving west and taming the land.
What the pioneers went through is not exaggerated in
this poem. The tone of the poem is serious and admiring. In "Davy Crockett's Dream," Crockett is a real historical figure who took on exaggerated legendary
qualities. His challenge is finding food in the freezing
cold. Exaggeration is present throughout the selection
as sneezes cause icicles to crackle in his nose, Oak
Wing pounds Crockett's head down between his shoul-
ders like a turtle, and his wife pokes him in the eye with
a long icicle hanging from her nose. The tone of this
story is much more humorous and silly. "Paul Bunyan"
is a totally fictional legend. He faces several challenges
like turning off the rain or the killing off the bee mosquitoes. He uses his wits and his strength to accomplish
huge tasks. The selection is all exaggerated and the tone
is one of awe and appreciation.

Difficulty: *Average*

Objective: *Essay*

23. Students should distinguish the genesis of the three
selections by pointing out that Stephen Vincent Benét
created "Western Wagons" as an original poem, probably
basing his creation on both oral and written reports that
made their way back east in the late nineteenth century
and the early twentieth century as pioneers moved west.
Students should note that Davy Crockett himself wrote
"Davy Crockett's Dream," probably basing his creation
on his own imagination and the tall-tale genre that was
establishing itself in America in the nineteenth century.
For "Paul Bunyan in the North Woods," the writer Carl
Sandburg collected and wrote down popular oral legends that were being passed by word of mouth. Students might add that Sandburg himself created the
opening paragraph from scratch. It offers his view of
how the stories he collected originated in the first place.
Although the three selections came about in different
ways, they have in common an appreciation for
the people—be they real or legendary—who took on
challenges as the country grew.

Difficulty: *Challenging*

Objective: *Essay*

Writing Workshop—Unit 6, Part 1

Multimedia Report: Integrating Grammar Skills, p. 98

A. 1. A. fragment
       B. sentence
    2. A. sentence
       B. run-on
    3. A. fragment
       B. sentence

B. Answers will vary.

1. We are studying American history; it is an interesting subject.
2. George Washington, a military leader, was our first president.
3. Abraham Lincoln was the sixteenth president. He gave a speech at Gettysburg.
4. After the assassination of Abraham Lincoln, Andrew Johnson became president.

Unit 6, Part 1 Answers

Benchmark Test 11, p. 99

MULTIPLE CHOICE

1. ANS: D
2. ANS: B
3. ANS: C
4. ANS: B
5. ANS: B
6. ANS: A
7. ANS: A
8. ANS: D
9. ANS: B
10. ANS: C
11. ANS: B
12. ANS: A
13. ANS: D
14. ANS: C
15. ANS: D
16. ANS: C
17. ANS: B
18. ANS: C
19. ANS: A
20. ANS: D
21. ANS: A
22. ANS: B
23. ANS: C
24. ANS: C
25. ANS: D
26. ANS: D
27. ANS: B
28. ANS: A
29. ANS: D
30. ANS: D
31. ANS: B
32. ANS: C
33. ANS: D

ESSAY

34. Students should choose a modern subject and explain it in mythic terms. To make the myth entertaining, they might include dialect, modern slang, idioms, and especially humor.

35. Students should discuss the character's personality, talents, and deeds as well as the effectiveness with which he or she is portrayed. They should cite specific examples from the work to support their general statements about it.

36. Students might list written material, illustrations, audio material, and video material that they would include in their reports. They should indicate several sources for their materials, perhaps including both library and on-line sources.

Unit 6, Part 2 Answers

Diagnostic Test 12, p. 106

MULTIPLE CHOICE

1. ANS: C
2. ANS: A
3. ANS: D
4. ANS: B
5. ANS: D
6. ANS: A
7. ANS: B
8. ANS: C
9. ANS: B
10. ANS: D
11. ANS: A
12. ANS: C
13. ANS: C
14. ANS: A
15. ANS: B

"Ellis Island" by Joseph Bruchac

Vocabulary Warm-up Exercises, p. 110

A.
1. slips
2. veins
3. knowledge
4. native
5. memory
6. sickness

B. Sample Answers

1. F; All *decades* are ten years long.
2. T; There are more independent countries than *empires* today.
3. T; When a foreign army has *invaded* and is occupying your country, it can be unsafe.

4. F; A *quarantine* is enforced when there is a danger-ous illness, and you should not go into or out of an area that is in *quarantine.*

5. F; *Slovak* people, who are from Slovakia, live in this country.

6. F; An *answerer* would make the wish come true.

Reading Warm-up A, p. 111

Sample Answers

1. (preserve, of the old country to pass something along to my children); The first *memory* I have is of my fourth birthday party at an amusement park.

2. the horrible things my native country's government did to its people in the name of security; I would rather not have the *knowledge* that my friend cheated on the math test.

3. (American-born); My *native* city is Mexico City, Mexico.

4. (health); The *sickness* I had that made me stay home for a week was chicken pox.

5. freedom, blood; *Veins* in my wrists are slightly raised bluish lines.

6. muffled paddles rowing smoothly across the water of a calm lake; A memory that *slips* through one's mind moves calmly and gently and probably does not cause a bad feeling.

Reading Warm-up B, p. 112

Sample Answers

1. (Those nearly sixty years); My baby brother was born in one of the last two *decades.*

2. southern, central, and eastern Europe; *Empires* are countries or groups of countries that are ruled by one person such as an emperor.

3. (men); I like going with my friend's family to the *Slovak* dance hall.

4. officials feared an outbreak of a serious illness that could come ashore; It would be frightening to live under *quarantine.* If you lived under *quarantine*, you wouldn't know if you were going to come down with some horrible disease and possibly die. You wouldn't be able to go ashore to join your family and friends.

5. (questioner); A candidate in a debate becomes an *answerer* of the audience's questions.

6. foreign armies; If the United States were *invaded*, I would be scared and very angry.

"Ellis Island" by Joseph Bruchac

Reading: Ask Questions to Set a Purpose for Reading, p. 113

1. Immigrants who came to the United States through Ellis Island had to spend some time in quarantine to be sure they were not carrying any contagious diseases.

2. The writer also has Native American grandparents, who did not come to the United States through Ellis Island, but were living here already.

Literary Analysis: Cultural Context, p. 114

1. His other ancestors are Native Americans.

2. Native Americans lived on lands that were invaded by Europeans coming to America. These original Ameri-cans lived close to the land.

3. Students may say that the cultural/historical context may be ancestry, respect for ancestors, immigration, or what makes an American. They should support their answers with details.

Vocabulary Builder, p. 115

A. 1. No, he or she would be called a Swede, someone *native* to Sweden.

2. No, you could not visit with your friends, because you would be separated from them.

3. No, an immigrant leaves his or her *native* land for another.

4. No, if ill people are separated from others, the illness will not spread.

B. 1. B; 2. D

Enrichment: An Immigration History, p. 118

1. 62 years

2. 100,000 (2,000,000 divided by 20)

3. 1880–1920

4. $45,000 ($30 multiplied by 1,500)

Selection Test A, p. 119

Critical Reading

1. ANS: B	DIF: Easy	OBJ: Reading
2. ANS: C	DIF: Easy	OBJ: Comprehension
3. ANS: A	DIF: Easy	OBJ: Literary Analysis
4. ANS: B	DIF: Easy	OBJ: Interpretation
5. ANS: D	DIF: Easy	OBJ: Interpretation
6. ANS: B	DIF: Easy	OBJ: Comprehension

Vocabulary and Grammar

7. ANS: B	DIF: Easy	OBJ: Vocabulary
8. ANS: A	DIF: Easy	OBJ: Vocabulary
9. ANS: A	DIF: Easy	OBJ: Grammar
10. ANS: D	DIF: Easy	OBJ: Grammar

Essay

11. Students' essay should reflect that the poet's European ancestors were members of a large group that came to America and invaded lands that other people had called

home for thousands of years. His Native American ancestors were inhabitants of these invaded lands. This makes the poet a product of two very different life experiences and worldviews that may be in conflict.

Difficulty: *Easy*
Objective: *Essay*

Selection Test B, p. 121

Critical Reading

1. ANS: D	DIF: Average	OBJ: Reading
2. ANS: B	DIF: Average	OBJ: Comprehension
3. ANS: B	DIF: Average	OBJ: Literary Analysis
4. ANS: D	DIF: Challenging	OBJ: Interpretation
5. ANS: D	DIF: Challenging	OBJ: Interpretation
6. ANS: C	DIF: Average	OBJ: Literary Analysis
7. ANS: A	DIF: Challenging	OBJ: Literary Analysis

Vocabulary and Grammar

8. ANS: A	DIF: Average	OBJ: Vocabulary
9. ANS: A	DIF: Average	OBJ: Vocabulary
10. ANS: B	DIF: Average	OBJ: Grammar

Essay

11. Students' essays should reflect the views of both European immigrants and Native Americans depicted in the poem. To the former, Ellis Island was a gateway to a land of dreams and ownership of land. To the later, it was a symbol of invasion and the takeover of the land on which they already lived.

Difficulty: *Average*
Objective: *Essay*

12. Students' essays should reflect these ideas, based on information in the poem: European immigrants believed in the idea of land ownership, but most of them had never been able to afford this dream. They saw Ellis Island/America as their doorway to realizing this dream. Native Americans did not believe in owning the land, but sharing it in common with others. When Europeans came, Native Americans saw their "lands invaded / when the earth became owned." This was an event that went against their view of how to live in the natural world.

Difficulty: *Challenging*
Objective: *Essay*

from *Out of the Dust* by Karen Hesse

Vocabulary Warm-up Exercises, p. 124

A. 1. harvest
   2. brewing
   3. dampen

   4. fleeing
   5. stumbled
   6. relief

B. Sample Answers

1. No, a train needs a *locomotive* in order to move, since this is its engine.
2. Yes, a very old table might be fragile with thin or *spindly* legs that could cause it to be wobbly or *rickety*.
3. A terrible *drought* results in an inability to grow crops, which could lead to food shortages.
4. *Feuding* is different from arguing since it often involves feelings of anger and is long-lasting.
5. Plants are *sparse* in a desert because it gets little rain.

Reading Warm-up A, p. 125

Sample Answers

1. small farmers in the United States; *Brewing* means "starting to happen soon."
2. (to find jobs); Lots of people were *fleeing* from Florida during the hurricanes of the summer of 2004.
3. churn out the crops at high speeds and with little waste; During *harvest*, people or machines gather ripe crops.
4. (Farmers in the twenty-first century); I felt *relief* when I found out that my grandmother did not have cancer after all.
5. through the fields at small "pick your own" farms; People might have *stumbled* over the uneven rows of crops, small rocks, or fallen fruit or vegetables.
6. (bandana); When I am hot, I *dampen* your face with cool water.

Reading Warm-up B, p. 126

Sample Answers

1. people, population; *Sparse* means "small in number and thinly spread out."
2. (lack of rain); A *drought* is a long period of time during which no rain falls.
3. without fertilization and adequate time to rest; A *spindly* plant would have a tall, thin stem and look weak.
4. (the few plots of good land that were left); When *feuding*, people feel very angry and might act in mean ways that they could regret later.
5. furniture; An old car in bad condition could be *rickety*.
6. (trains); A *locomotive* might whistle and sound like a big wind blowing by.

from _Out of the Dust_ by Karen Hesse

Reading: Ask Questions to Set a Purpose for Reading, p. 127

1. The Roosevelt administration loaned farmers money to plant their wheat crop and didn't ask for repayment until the crop was harvested.
2. Some farmers left the Dust Bowl to become migrant workers elsewhere.

Literary Analysis: Cultural Context, p. 128

1. The father says that it's sure to rain soon and then he can get a new crop of wheat to grow. The mother points out that it hasn't rained enough to grow wheat in three years.
2. The mother explains that even a little rain keeps people hoping, and even without the rain, when spring comes a farmer has to believe his crops will do well that year.

Vocabulary Builder, p. 129

A. 1. No, if they're _feuding_, they're fighting.
2. No, a rhino and a hippo have strong thick legs, not _spindly_ legs.
3. No, vegetables and flowers need water, and a _drought_ is a dry period.
4. Yes, a newborn baby usually has _sparse_, or little, hair.
5. Yes, a _rickety_ stepladder would be likely to break and should be repaired.

B. 1. B; 2. D; 3. A; 4. C; 5. D

Enrichment: Into the Dust, p. 132

Students should use imagery and vivid language to convey the sense of having lived through a natural disaster or significant weather event.

"Ellis Island" by Joseph Bruchac
from _Out of the Dust_ by Karen Hesse

Build Language Skills: Vocabulary, p. 133

A. 1. bayou
2. barbecue
3. chipmunk
4. raccoon
5. chocolate

B. 1. My teacher liked my report, so I did not have to _revise_ it.
2. The actress was disappointed by the negative _critique_ of her performance.
3. I opened my eyes wide so I could _focus_ on the picture.
4. It took just a few minutes for me to _skim_ the story to find the theme.
5. These clear photos will help the woman _identify_ her friend from college.

Build Language Skills: Grammar, p. 134

A. 1. Immigrants come to America for several reasons; many are looking for economic opportunity.
2. The young boy took his favorite items out of his trunk: photographs of his family, a cap knitted by his grandmother, and a small telescope.
3. no change (leave as is)
4. Each immigrant was examined by a doctor; those who were healthy were free to go.
5. The immigrant family unwrapped their lunch: potato pie, cheese, and apples.

B. Students should draw from their experiences and correctly use semicolons and colons.

---

from _Out of the Dust_ by Karen Hesse

Selection Test A, p. 135

Critical Reading

1. ANS: D	DIF: Easy	OBJ: Reading
2. ANS: D	DIF: Easy	OBJ: Comprehension
3. ANS: A	DIF: Easy	OBJ: Interpretation
4. ANS: B	DIF: Easy	OBJ: Literary Analysis
5. ANS: C	DIF: Easy	OBJ: Interpretation
6. ANS: B	DIF: Easy	OBJ: Comprehension
7. ANS: B	DIF: Easy	OBJ: Interpretation
8. ANS: D	DIF: Easy	OBJ: Interpretation
9. ANS: B	DIF: Easy	OBJ: Reading
10. ANS: C	DIF: Easy	OBJ: Literary Analysis
11. ANS: C	DIF: Easy	OBJ: Literary Analysis

Vocabulary and Grammar

12. ANS: C	DIF: Easy	OBJ: Vocabulary
13. ANS: A	DIF: Easy	OBJ: Grammar

Essay

14. Students' essays might focus on one or more of the following ideas: The Dust Bowl experience affected the narrator's relationship with her parents; it affected the parents' relationship with one another; it affected all the neighbors, many of whom left the area; it controlled everything the family did. The narrator uses figurative language to help readers see how the Dust Bowl experience affected everything about her life. She describes how the dust looked, sounded, and felt, and how completely it ruled all aspects of the family's life. Students may use a variety of examples from the text as support for their ideas.

Difficulty: _Easy_
Objective: _Essay_

15. Students' essays may reflect any of the following: A person growing up in the Dust Bowl life might have become either very committed to lasting it out—as her father did—or committed to making a change—as her migrant neighbors did. A person might have come to feel that he/she could not change things or might have an optimistic view of life, thinking that the rain would have to come sometime.

Difficulty: *Easy*
Objective: *Essay*

Selection Test B, p. 138

Critical Reading

1. ANS: B	DIF: Average	OBJ: Reading
2. ANS: A	DIF: Challenging	OBJ: Literary Analysis
3. ANS: B	DIF: Average	OBJ: Reading
4. ANS: B	DIF: Average	OBJ: Comprehension
5. ANS: D	DIF: Challenging	OBJ: Interpretation
6. ANS: C	DIF: Average	OBJ: Literary Analysis
7. ANS: A	DIF: Average	OBJ: Reading
8. ANS: D	DIF: Challenging	OBJ: Interpretation
9. ANS: D	DIF: Average	OBJ: Interpretation
10. ANS: A	DIF: Challenging	OBJ: Literary Analysis
11. ANS: B	DIF: Average	OBJ: Reading
12. ANS: B	DIF: Average	OBJ: Interpretation
13. ANS: A	DIF: Challenging	OBJ: Interpretation
14. ANS: C	DIF: Challenging	OBJ: Literary Analysis
15. ANS: B	DIF: Average	OBJ: Comprehension

Vocabulary and Grammar

16. ANS: C	DIF: Average	OBJ: Vocabulary
17. ANS: C	DIF: Average	OBJ: Vocabulary
18. ANS: C	DIF: Average	OBJ: Grammar
19. ANS: A	DIF: Challenging	OBJ: Grammar

Essay

20. Students may think that without some kind of healthy faith in the future, the farmer would have given up and he and his family would have suffered even more. Students who think the farmer's belief was unhealthy may say that if he had been more realistic, he and his family could have accompanied the migrants and perhaps found better conditions elsewhere.

Difficulty: *Average*
Objective: *Essay*

21. Students' essays should reflect the reality of Dust Bowl homes: they needed constant cleaning, sweeping, and blocking of the dust. Like Daddy, people probably sneezed dust, coughed dust, and cried dusty tears.

Some situations today that students might use as comparison are smog, oil spills, floods, hurricanes, tornadoes, and so on.

Difficulty: *Challenging*
Objective: *Essay*

22. Students' essays should reflect that the historical context may change but the problems remain similar. People who lived in the Dust Bowl times suffered from failure of their crops and the resulting economic insecurity. Their outlook on life was largely determined by such conditions—they might despair or they might keep having hope. Students might compare this historical situation with the buying up of family farms by agricultural corporations, leaving many farm families out of work and causing them to lose their land; the moving of many jobs overseas, leaving millions of workers without a regular income; and so on.

Difficulty: *Challenging*
Objective: *Essay*

"Choice: A Tribute to Dr. Martin Luther King, Jr." by Alice Walker

Vocabulary Warm-up Exercises, p. 142

A. 1. heritage
2. importance
3. inherited
4. cemetery
5. capable
6. fearless
7. resistance
8. rotted

B. Sample Answers
1. My *ancestral* home and my *birthplace* would be the same if I were born where my family had lived for generations.
2. Keeping someone *handcuffed* for a long time, in a harmful position, or under extreme weather conditions are examples of *brutality*.
3. *Municipal* leaders might *acknowledge* brave firefighters by giving them keys to the city.
4. The *abandonment* of life's *realities* is dangerous because living in a fantasy world and not dealing with what is real is not a healthy way to live.

Reading Warm-up A, p. 143

Sample Answers
1. (land, culture); Two parts of my *heritage* are my religion and my belief that it is important to help those not as fortunate as me.
2. cannot overstate; Being able to go to a good college is of great *importance* to me.

3. from his father; My mother *inherited* some money from her parents.

4. (going along with); I have a great *resistance* to my parents making me do my sister's chores.

5. where all those dead folks are buried; The rain began as we walked through the *graveyard*, but we were not yet ready to leave the *burial ground* of our favorite rock star.

6. (able); I am *capable* of memorizing music and holding my breath underwater.

7. afraid; I am *fearless* when I jump off the high diving board.

8. She said she wanted us to move before our brains *crumbled* away.

Reading Warm-up B, p. 144

Sample Answers

1. (cities); A *municipal* service in my town is trash collection.

2. (*birth*, *place*); My *birthplace* is a little town sixty miles from Denver, Colorado.

3. continue to live; The effects of *abandonment* on a house include break-ins, rotting, homeless people living there, leaks, and finally collapse.

4. (homeland); My *ancestral* language is Polish.

5. (*real*); Three *realities* of life are studying hard to graduate, trying to get into a good college, and dealing with death.

6. violence; An act of *brutality* is beating a person.

7. (they [protesters]); Two things a *handcuffed* person cannot do are eat with a knife and fork and put on a shirt.

8. (the demonstrators were winning); I *acknowledge* that I must work harder in school if I'm going to learn everything I need to know.

"Choice: A Tribute to Dr. Martin Luther King, Jr." by Alice Walker

Reading: Set a Purpose for Reading and Adjust Your Reading Rate, p. 145

1. to learn his ideas and opinions
2. slow, with rereading of specific passages
3. to be entertained
4. normal speed, or even quicker
5. to be entertained
6. normal speed, or even quicker
7. to learn the author's ideas about Walker's work
8. slow, with rereading of specific passages

Literary Analysis: Author's Influences, p. 146

1. Dr. Martin Luther King, Jr.
2. She was impressed by his courage.

3. America saw Alice Walker and other African Americans as people who did not have the same rights or freedoms as white Americans.

Vocabulary Builder, p. 147

A. Sample Answers

1. She would enjoy going to plays, because she has an artistic outlook.
2. Yes, Dr. King's work helped gain important rights for African Americans.
3. The group has fewer rights than other groups.

B. 1. A; 2. C; 3. D

Enrichment: The Words of Dr. Martin Luther King, Jr., p. 150

1. D; 2. B; 3. C; 4. A

Selection Test A, p. 151

Critical Reading

1. ANS: A	DIF: Easy	OBJ: Reading
2. ANS: D	DIF: Easy	OBJ: Literary Analysis
3. ANS: B	DIF: Easy	OBJ: Literary Analysis
4. ANS: C	DIF: Easy	OBJ: Reading
5. ANS: B	DIF: Easy	OBJ: Literary Analysis
6. ANS: A	DIF: Easy	OBJ: Comprehension
7. ANS: C	DIF: Easy	OBJ: Reading
8. ANS: C	DIF: Easy	OBJ: Comprehension
9. ANS: D	DIF: Easy	OBJ: Interpretation
10. ANS: C	DIF: Easy	OBJ: Comprehension

Vocabulary and Grammar

11. ANS: B	DIF: Easy	OBJ: Vocabulary
12. ANS: B	DIF: Easy	OBJ: Grammar

Essay

13. Students may say that when students reach high-school age they are ready to be more open to the world. For Alice Walker and other African-American students in the early 1960s, the effects of the actions taken by Dr. King and others must have been earth-shattering. Students may also say that people can be affected by historical movements at any age, so Walker's age was no more important in affecting how she was moved by Dr. King and his work than the age of her parents or the age of younger students.

Difficulty: *Easy*

Objective: *Essay*

14. Students may cite King's courage, his willingness to be arrested for his actions, his confrontation with the injustices toward African Americans, his power as a preacher,

tices toward African Americans, his power as a preacher, his concern for all who were disinherited, or his absence of interest in prizes and awards as important reasons for admiring him.

Difficulty: *Easy*
Objective: *Essay*

Selection Test B, p. 154

Critical Reading

1. ANS: C	DIF: Challenging	OBJ: Reading
2. ANS: B	DIF: Easy	OBJ: Reading
3. ANS: B	DIF: Challenging	OBJ: Literary Analysis
4. ANS: A	DIF: Challenging	OBJ: Interpretation
5. ANS: A	DIF: Average	OBJ: Literary Analysis
6. ANS: A	DIF: Average	OBJ: Reading
7. ANS: D	DIF: Challenging	OBJ: Interpretation
8. ANS: C	DIF: Average	OBJ: Interpretation
9. ANS: C	DIF: Average	OBJ: Literary Analysis
10. ANS: C	DIF: Challenging	OBJ: Comprehension
11. ANS: B	DIF: Challenging	OBJ: Literary Analysis
12. ANS: D	DIF: Challenging	OBJ: Interpretation

Vocabulary

13. ANS: B	DIF: Average	OBJ: Vocabulary
14. ANS: D	DIF: Average	OBJ: Vocabulary
15. ANS: A	DIF: Average	OBJ: Grammar
16. ANS: C	DIF: Challenging	OBJ: Vocabulary and Grammar

Essay

17. Students' essays should reflect that according to Walker, King gave African Americans back their heritage. Instead of moving north, they could stay in the South and claim their rights, or come back to the South as residents, not visitors. He gave African Americans a sense of having a real history in a place, the American South.

Difficulty: *Challenging*
Objective: *Essay*

18. Students' may say that they read the essay slowly for the purpose of learning how Dr. King influenced Alice Walker's life as a southern African American woman. Rereading might be necessary to be clear about which historical period she is talking about at different times within the speech.

Difficulty: *Average*
Objective: *Essay*

19. Students' essays should reflect their own knowledge of some of the effects of the civil rights movement on the lives of African Americans and all Americans, such as an end to segregated facilities throughout the South and elsewhere; a Voting Rights bill to guarantee the vote to all Americans; open housing and equal employment opportunity laws; and so on. From the essay, one major public act visible "all around" the speaker and the listeners is the site of the speech—a restaurant that would have barred African American customers before the Civil Rights Movement made such an action illegal.

Difficulty: *Challenging*
Objective: *Essay*

"An Episode of War" by Stephen Crane

Vocabulary Warm-up Exercises, p. 158

A. 1. assault
2. ambulances
3. assistance
4. encouragement
5. representatives
6. corps
7. engaged
8. menace

B. Sample Answers

1. A *bugler* would keep his instrument in a case, but not in a *scabbard* as that is a case for a sword.
2. If the *lieutenant* is yelling at his troops, he is angry, and therefore, wouldn't be doing it *sympathetically*.
3. *Spectators* at a sporting match watch the game or race; they don't take part in it.
4. You would probably be falling if you were to go *headlong* down the stairs. Therefore, walking down the stairs is safer.
5. If I were among the *stragglers*, I'd be one of the last to get back to the bus.
6. If I liked doing things alone, I would not like being part of a *squad*, which is a small group.

Reading Warm-up A, p. 159

Sample Answers

1. (their country); My sister got a bad cramp while swimming in the lake, and I came to her *assistance*, pulling her back to shore.
2. (cash awards); Knowing that my friends are behind me gives me *encouragement*.
3. (of all states and all walks of life); The student council has *representatives* from all the homeroom classes.

4. <u>enemy</u>; A modern *assault* during wartime is often in the form of a bombing.

5. <u>wagons used to remove the sick and injured from the battlefield</u>; Modern *ambulances* are large vans with modern life-saving equipment and are staffed by emergency medical technicians.

6. (southern states' seceding or withdrawing, from the Union); The Ebola virus is a modern-day *menace*.

7. (draft dodging); Some *took part* in draft dodging, or avoiding being taken into the army.

8. <u>soldiers</u>; *Corps* means "a small group of people, such as a group of soldiers."

Reading Warm-up B, p. 160

Sample Answers

1. (doctors); My friends and I were *spectators* at the high school basketball games this season.

2. The foot soldiers are lower in rank, and the generals higher. But a *bugler* is someone who plays a bugle, or trumpet-like instrument, and a *lieutenant* is an officer.

3. <u>soldiers</u>; The best *squad* in the army had a majority of women in it.

4. <u>sword pulled from</u>; Without a *scabbard*, you could easily hurt yourself on the sword blade.

5. (soldiers on foot); I went *headlong* down the water slide.

6. <u>quickly</u>; If a group were walking in a dangerous area and it was getting dark, *stragglers* could put themselves in danger by lagging behind the rest of the group.

7. (They made the unbearable just a little bearable.); When my grandfather died, the people who came to visit acted *sympathetically* toward us.

"An Episode of War" by Stephen Crane

Reading: Set a Purpose for Reading and Adjust Your Reading Rate, p. 161

1. to be informed about how characters act during a battle and learn what war is like from the soldier's point of view

2. slowly, including rereading, to understand long and formal sentences and unfamiliar information

3. to learn about when and where the battles were fought and what the battlefields looked and sounded like

4. slowly, including rereading, to understand long and formal sentences and unfamiliar information

5. to learn about what the Vietnam War was like for the soldiers

6. normal or fast, because the story is written in modern times and probably uses familiar language and references

7. to be entertained or educated by soldiers' stories

8. normal or fast, because the story would have lots of dialogue and probably use familiar language and references

Literary Analysis: Author's Influences, p. 162

1. C; 2. A; 3. B; 4. C

Vocabulary Builder, p. 163

A. Sample Answers

1. I would feel strange, because I would not want to be forced to attend a party.

2. Someone who was already feeling upset would not handle a surprise well.

3. If a friend lied to me, I would have contempt for him or her.

B. 1. B; 2. C; 3. D

Enrichment: Media Messages, p. 166

Students should mention that Crane describes the horrors of war in this passage, with no sense of glory or honor. They may contrast Crane's message with the message of a modern movie or video game that glorifies war, or they may say that they have seen a realistic movie that affects them much like Crane's writing, in that it shows terrible details.

"Choice: A Tribute to Dr. Martin Luther King, Jr." by Alice Walker
"An Episode of War" by Stephen Crane

Build Language Skills: Vocabulary, p. 167

A. 1. salsa
2. frankfurter, sauerkraut
3. chowder
4. chili con carne
5. salad

B. 1. The witness was unable to *identify* the man she saw running from the fire.

2. Don't *skim* through the story or you'll miss the humor.

3. I'm trying to *focus* on my homework, so please turn down the radio.

4. We'll have to *revise* our plans for the building.

5. Please prepare a *critique* of the movie you saw last night.

Build Language Skills: Grammar, p. 168

A. 1. Alice Walker's life was deeply affected by Dr. Martin Luther King, Jr., the civil rights leader.

2. She loved to hear him preach at Ebenezer Baptist Church.

3. Alice was changed when she watched two African American students try to enroll at the University of Georgia.

4. She says that many black Americans feel more comfortable in the South because of Dr. King's life.

B. Students should write about a person who has been important to them. Their writing should have proper capitalization.

"An Episode of War" by Stephen Crane

Selection Test A, p. 169

Critical Reading

1. ANS: B	DIF: Easy	OBJ: Reading
2. ANS: D	DIF: Easy	OBJ: Reading
3. ANS: C	DIF: Easy	OBJ: Reading
4. ANS: D	DIF: Easy	OBJ: Interpretation
5. ANS: C	DIF: Easy	OBJ: Literary Analysis
6. ANS: D	DIF: Easy	OBJ: Comprehension
7. ANS: A	DIF: Easy	OBJ: Literary Analysis
8. ANS: D	DIF: Easy	OBJ: Interpretation
9. ANS: B	DIF: Easy	OBJ: Comprehension
10. ANS: B	DIF: Easy	OBJ: Comprehension

Vocabulary and Grammar

11. ANS: C	DIF: Easy	OBJ: Vocabulary
12. ANS: A	DIF: Easy	OBJ: Grammar

Essay

13. Students may say that the lieutenant's fellow soldiers are sympathetic to him because they are all in the same position. Any one of them could be wounded at any time. The medical staff, however, is safely away from the fighting. They are overworked and cannot deal with the wounds of war. So each wounded soldier is just another way to show them how helpless they are.

   Difficulty: *Easy*

   Objective: *Essay*

14. Students may suggest one or more of the following purposes: to learn more about the Civil War, to learn about how soldiers responded to the effects of war, to experience the sights, sounds, and feelings of what it was like for soldiers in battle, and so on.

   Difficulty: *Easy*

   Objective: *Essay*

Selection Test B, p. 172

Critical Reading

1. ANS: C	DIF: Average	OBJ: Reading
2. ANS: B	DIF: Average	OBJ: Comprehension
3. ANS: C	DIF: Average	OBJ: Reading
4. ANS: D	DIF: Average	OBJ: Interpretation
5. ANS: D	DIF: Challenging	OBJ: Interpretation
6. ANS: B	DIF: Challenging	OBJ: Comprehension
7. ANS: C	DIF: Average	OBJ: Literary Analysis
8. ANS: C	DIF: Average	OBJ: Literary Analysis
9. ANS: D	DIF: Average	OBJ: Literary Analysis
10. ANS: B	DIF: Average	OBJ: Literary Analysis
11. ANS: A	DIF: Challenging	OBJ: Interpretation
12. ANS: A	DIF: Average	OBJ: Reading

Vocabulary and Grammar

13. ANS: C	DIF: Average	OBJ: Vocabulary
14. ANS: A	DIF: Average	OBJ: Grammar
15. ANS: C	DIF: Challenging	OBJ: Grammar

Essay

16. Students' essays should reflect that the view of war in "An Episode of War" shows it in a real light. Battles are messy. Soldiers get shot both in and out of battle. Battlefield medical care is not very good. Students should recognize that sometimes war novels, war films, and war games focus largely on bravery and adventure instead of pain and suffering.

   Difficulty: *Average*

   Objective: *Essay*

17. Students' essays should note that although soldiers expect to be wounded during wartime, they generally are wounded in battle. The lieutenant's wound, which leads to the loss of his arm, is not received in battle but is the result of a stray bullet that hits him while he is eating breakfast.

   Difficulty: *Challenging*

   Objective: *Essay*

from *My Own True Name* by Pat Mora
"Words to Sit In, Like Chairs"
by Naomi Shihab Nye

Vocabulary Warm-up Exercises, p. 176

A.
1. involved
2. enabled
3. discovering
4. beacons
5. phrases
6. topic
7. collectors
8. betrayed

B. Sample Answers
1. Several of my friends had *sorrowful* expressions when we learned that a popular senior at the high school had been badly hurt in a car crash.

2. One *basic* rule people should follow to avoid being *obnoxious* is to chew their food with their mouths closed.

3. I own a *miniature* version of a hot rod which even has working doors!

4. Award shows build excitement before they *reveal* winners by using loud music and by delaying the announcement several times.

5. It is *inappropriate* to open any mail that is addressed to someone else, because it is private and not been written for you to see.

6. All advertisements try to *tempt* you to buy the product.

Reading Warm-up A, p. 177

Sample Answers

1. failed or quit; Right now I am *involved* in the school chorus, which I really enjoy.

2. (perfect); *Phrases* are groups of words with special meanings.

3. Creativity and ease of words; The writer compares these things to friends since you are most often *betrayed* by friends or those you trust.

4. (the voice that they had lost); I am now in the process of *discovering* lots of information about U.S. history.

5. music; A *topic* that I often read and write about is the courage of people in unusual situations.

6. (lighthouse); *Beacons* are beams of light coming from lighthouses located along the shoreline and lock like bright beams welcoming home boats and ships.

7. Being *collectors* of useful names has *enabled* beginning writers to promote themselves, which helps them find work when they do not have assignments.

Reading Warm-up B, p. 178

Sample Answers

1. These ten amendments [Bill of Rights]; I believe a *basic* right that is especially important is the right to practice a religion of choice.

2. (for the government to make laws restricting what people say or write); I once saw a coach roughly shove a player onto the bench, which I think is an *inappropriate* use of power.

3. their sources; *Reveal* means "to make known or to show."

4. (these freedoms); Our *unique* freedom to express ourselves with any words we want means that people feel free to write anything, even if what they write is *obnoxious*.

5. the pitfalls of too much power; For some reason, it seems to be human nature that power will *tempt* people to do unfair things to those less powerful.

6. (book burnings, or the murder of writers who have spoken against the government); To me, the most *sorrowful* scene in the list in the murder of people for expressing their opinions.

7. I believe that every classroom in the United States is a *miniature* representation of the freedom to get an education.

from *My Own True Name* by Pat Mora
"Words to Sit In, Like Chairs"
by Naomi Shihab Nye

Literary Analysis: Comparing Works on a Similar Theme, p. 179

Sample Answers

1. Open letter; essay

2. Mora is writing a letter as if directly speaking to students to encourage them to practice writing all the time and to like writing; Shihab Nye is writing an essay to explain how writing helps her deal with emotions and life and to encourage others to write their feelings.

3. Theme of both—using words to express oneself.

4. *Mora's main points:* write what's inside of you, read to become a better writer, practice writing often and anywhere, pay attention to what's going on around you, write to know yourself better, and never speak badly about your writing; *Nye's main points:* use words to express what happens in your life, use words—written or spoken—to comfort and encourage yourself and others, use words to make sense out of life and clear your mind, use words to make you feel better, and use words to help balance the big things in life.

5. Both writers believe in using words all the time and to write to know yourself better and express what is happening inside of you and around you.

6. Mora approaches the theme of self-expression by explaining why she writes and by encouraging students to practice writing all the time; Nye approaches the theme of self-expression by describing the emotional experience of 9/11, by using words to help her get through the emotions of the tragedy, and by encouraging others to use words to deal with life.

Vocabulary Builder, p. 180

A. Sample Answers

1. frightening; The large crowd that has assembled may be very intimidating, or frightening, for an inexperienced speaker.

2. able to speak two languages; Maria translates Spanish into English at the Spanish embassy because she is bilingual.

3. secretly listening; Whenever we go to a restaurant, Carina tries eavesdropping, or secretly listening, to the conversation of people at the next table.

4. seriously; Because Michael considered the test serious, he entered the exam room soberly.

5. confusion; The classroom was in turmoil, or confusion, after the pet hamster escaped from its cage.
6. signals; The ranger built signal fires as beacons to guide the lost hikers back to the campsite.

B. 1. C; 2. D; 3. B; 4. A

Selection Test A, p. 182

Critical Reading

1. ANS: A	DIF: Easy	OBJ: Interpretation
2. ANS: C	DIF: Easy	OBJ: Comprehension
3. ANS: D	DIF: Easy	OBJ: Interpretation
4. ANS: B	DIF: Easy	OBJ: Comprehension
5. ANS: A	DIF: Easy	OBJ: Comprehension
6. ANS: C	DIF: Easy	OBJ: Comprehension
7. ANS: A	DIF: Easy	OBJ: Interpretation
8. ANS: C	DIF: Easy	OBJ: Interpretation
9. ANS: D	DIF: Easy	OBJ: Literary Analysis
10. ANS: A	DIF: Easy	OBJ: Literary Analysis
11. ANS: B	DIF: Easy	OBJ: Literary Analysis
12. ANS: C	DIF: Easy	OBJ: Literary Analysis

Vocabulary

13. ANS: B	DIF: Easy	OBJ: Vocabulary
14. ANS: D	DIF: Easy	OBJ: Vocabulary
15. ANS: C	DIF: Easy	OBJ: Vocabulary

Essay

16. Students should be able to acknowledge that both writers think of words as powerful and writing words or speaking words as a way to help ourselves in good times and bad times. Both writers see words as a way to reach out and share—a way to understand each other. They also see words as a way to get to know what we ourselves are feeling. Mora and Nye would mostly agree.
   Difficulty: *Easy*
   Objective: *Essay*

17. Mora discusses reading and writing from childhood to the present. For example, she tells readers that she read comic books in grade school and with her sisters and brothers climbed all over her aunt, the storyteller. Nye tells of her personal experience when she heard about the terrorist attack of September 11, 2001, and in the days after. She explains where she was and with whom; she tells us about the gift one student gave her—a collapsible hamper; and she tells us that she had telephone conversations with other people trying to make sense of the event.
   Difficulty: *Easy*
   Objective: *Essay*

Selection Test B, p. 185

Critical Reading

1. ANS: B	DIF: Average	OBJ: Comprehension
2. ANS: C	DIF: Challenging	OBJ: Comprehension
3. ANS: A	DIF: Challenging	OBJ: Interpretation
4. ANS: D	DIF: Average	OBJ: Interpretation
5. ANS: B	DIF: Average	OBJ: Interpretation
6. ANS: D	DIF: Average	OBJ: Comprehension
7. ANS: A	DIF: Average	OBJ: Interpretation
8. ANS: B	DIF: Average	OBJ: Comprehension
9. ANS: C	DIF: Challenging	OBJ: Interpretation
10. ANS: B	DIF: Challenging	OBJ: Comprehension
11. ANS: D	DIF: Average	OBJ: Literary Analysis
12. ANS: B	DIF: Average	OBJ: Literary Analysis
13. ANS: D	DIF: Challenging	OBJ: Literary Analysis
14. ANS: B	DIF: Challenging	OBJ: Literary Analysis
15. ANS: C	DIF: Average	OBJ: Literary Analysis
16. ANS: A	DIF: Average	OBJ: Literary Analysis

Vocabulary

17. ANS: B	DIF: Average	OBJ: Vocabulary
18. ANS: B	DIF: Average	OBJ: Vocabulary
19. ANS: D	DIF: Average	OBJ: Vocabulary
20. ANS: D	DIF: Average	OBJ: Vocabulary

Essay

21. The theme in both works is the importance of using words to express oneself. Both writers believe that using words is important and helpful. Both writers use words all the time in their own lives, and both want to express to others how using words can help them deal with what is happing inside of themselves as well as around them. The difference is that Mora explains in general why she writes and encourages others to write while Nye focuses specifically on the emotions she experienced on and after September 11, 2001, and how words helped her to make sense of the tragedy. Students will have various answers as to what each author's ideas made them think about the theme.
   Difficulty: *Average*
   Objective: *Essay*

22. The excerpt from Mora's work *My Own True Name* is an open letter written to her readers. It makes readers feel as if she is speaking directly to them and encouraging them personally. "Words to Sit In, Like Chairs" is an essay and seems to be more of a description of how the author deals with tragedy than direct advice to her audience.
   Difficulty: *Average*
   Objective: *Essay*

23. Mora reveals that she has always loved reading and writing but admits that she didn't make time to write until after she became a mother. Nye began writing down her thoughts in a notebook when she was six years old. Mora writes because it helps her know who she is, what is important to her, what makes her sad, and what makes her feel great. Nye writes to shape her experiences of things and to help her live, breathe, and see. Mora believes writing helps the writer know himself or herself better. Nye believes writing helps the writer share feelings and ease feelings of sorrow that are too big to grasp. Mora believes writing can help the world to bring their "inside voice out and let us hear" them. Nye believes that writing can help people deal with emotions better than taking action, especially violent action. Students' opinions on which writer is more compelling or persuasive will vary; they should explain their opinions.

Difficulty: *Challenging*
Objective: *Essay*

Writing Workshop—Unit 6, Part 2

Cause-and-Effect Essay: Integrating Grammar Skills, p. 189

A. 1. This is a long quote. There should be a colon after the first line. The exact words of Lincoln should be indented on the left and have no quotation marks.

B. 1. In a debate with Stephen Douglas, Abraham Lincoln said, "A house divided against itself cannot stand."

2. In his Inaugural Address on March 4, 1861, Abraham Lincoln said, ". . . the Union of these States is perpetual."

Spelling Workshop—Unit 6

Vowel Sounds in Unstressed Syllables, p. 190

A. 1. semester
2. politician
3. mediocre
4. evidence
5. magnificent
6. leisure
7. deficient
8. accurate

B. Sample Answers
1. An article about the difference between a good and a bad vacation should contain evidence about the amount of leisure time spent. Some may think a magnificent vacation would be a week at the beach. With rain every day that same vacation may end up being mediocre.

2. A student can improve deficient grades by limiting leisure time and increasing the amount of time

devoted to studying. Within a semester, mediocre grades will become magnificent grades with effort. A lasting, permanent effect of studying is true learning.

3. politician will need to be accurate in his or her information in order to get my vote. One who is deficient in evidence relating to claims against an opponent will not get much support. An article in a newspaper should not support one politician over another.

Unit 6, Part 2 Answers

Benchmark Test 12, p. 193

MULTIPLE CHOICE

1. ANS: A
2. ANS: A
3. ANS: C
4. ANS: C
5. ANS: D
6. ANS: A
7. ANS: D
8. ANS: A
9. ANS: B
10. ANS: A
11. ANS: B
12. ANS: B
13. ANS: C
14. ANS: B
15. ANS: C
16. ANS: D
17. ANS: D
18. ANS: A
19. ANS: C
20. ANS: D
21. ANS: A
22. ANS: D
23. ANS: B
24. ANS: C
25. ANS: D
26. ANS: A
27. ANS: D
28. ANS: A
29. ANS: A
30. ANS: D
31. ANS: C
32. ANS: A

ESSAY

33. Students should write questions that seem useful for researching the period they choose. They should list research sources and briefly explain why those sources might provide the information they need.

34. Students should include factual historical information as well as their opinions about it. They should indicate the qualities or achievements that they admire in the person and give details that support or illustrate their statements.

35. Students should explain how one or more events or situations resulted in one or more other events or situations. They should supply accurate facts and provide sufficient details to make the events clear. They should use transition words such as *because, since,* and *therefore* to make the cause-and-effect organization clear.

CURRICULUM